22.2.22

JOIN WITH US
a collection of stories for
the primary school assembly

JOIN WITH US
a collection of stories for
the primary school assembly

Jeanne L Jackson

STANLEY
THORNES

First published in 1987 by Basil Blackwell Ltd
Reprinted 1988, 1989, 1990, 1991

Reprinted in 1993 (twice), 1994 by
Simon & Schuster Education

Reprinted in 1995 by
Stanley Thornes (Publishers) Ltd, Ellenborough House, Wellington Street, Cheltenham
GL50 1YD, England

A catalogue record for this book is available from the British Library.

ISBN 0 7487 2374 9

Typeset in 10 on 12pt Times Roman
by Multiplex Techniques Ltd, St Mary Gray, Kent.

Printed in Great Britain by BPC Wheatons Ltd, Exeter

Contents

Introduction

Join with us is a collection of lively, imaginative, and frequently informative stories for children in the primary school. All the stories contain a moral or teaching point on such issues as give and take, co-operation, getting along with people, fair play, honesty etc. and can be read equally well to large or small groups of children, in the classroom or in the assembly hall.

The stories help teach children the skills of living together harmoniously in the communities of classroom, school and society, and can be used with children from various ethnic origins.

The author believes strongly in the importance of assemblies bringing unity and continuity to the primary school, and providing the children with a moral code suited to their school community. To this end, the stories are arranged in weekly themes which closely follow the school calendar. Many of the themes lead naturally and logically into the text. However, all the stories with the exception of 'Joseph' can be read in isolation from one another if preferred.

Each weekly theme is explored through three stories, all with simple prayers and hymn suggestions for those readers wanting complete self-contained assemblies. Each story has an introduction and a conclusion in a conversational style, which is easily adapted by the person telling it. Several stories have additional footnotes suggesting simple and quickly-prepared visual aids, to help bring the stories alive and to provide a focal point.

All the stories are original or are new adaptations of traditional tales and fables. It is the author's intention that all the stories should be enjoyed by both children and teachers, so that in enjoyment they *Join with us*.

Dedicated to the memory of Martha Conner

Acknowledgements

I wish to express grateful thanks to

- my three deputies, Miss I. Mawer, Miss V.A. Pennington (now head of White Laith Primary School), and Mrs J. Worsfold; for sharing the assemblies, and bringing to them their own skills, expertise and ideas.
- the staff and especially the children of Cobden Primary School; for their eager participation in all the assemblies and for being a source of inspiration and joy.
- Mr C. Roome, my predecessor at Cobden, under whose headship I received much advice, help and encouragement.
- Mrs E. Milner; for transforming a somewhat messy manuscript into a tidy typescript, and
- Val; for her (mostly!) patient support during the preparation of this book.

Hymn Book References

Reference has been made to the following hymn books:

A	Apusskidu	A & C Black
C&S	Come and Sing	Scripture Union
CGC	Carol gaily carol	A & C Black
ChP	Children Praising	Oxford University Press
C&P	Come and Praise	BBC Publications
MHB	Morning has broken	Schofield and Sims
OBC	Oxford book of carols	Oxford University Press
SFJ	Sing for joy	EMI Music
SSL	Someone's singing Lord	A & C Black

Autumn Term

The jigsaw

Week 1   Beginnings

Jigsaws are familiar to most children of primary school age, which is why I chose them for the first assembly, when everything is still strange and new. I showed the children a selection of jigsaws, ranging from a very simple slot-in-shape nursery puzzle, to a 1000-piece monster. I then chose a simple 50-piece puzzle and two children who could be relied upon to perform in front of others, and complete the jigsaw in a few minutes.

During the holidays, I came in to school several times to do some work. The building was here next to the playground and playing field. The classrooms were all here with the tables and chairs, cupboards and worktops. The caretaker and cleaners were here, getting everything clean for the new term, and some of the teachers were here, getting their classrooms and their books ready. But even with all those things and people here, something was missing. Do you know what it was?

Yes, there were no children here: so the school in the holidays wasn't a school at all, it was just a building. Without the children our school is not a school. Now that the new term has begun, and we are *all* here, it is a school again. It is good to have all our school family together again.

Our school reminds me of this jigsaw. Here it is in its box, there are quite a number of pieces to it. Perhaps two of the older children could come out to the table, and do this jigsaw for me, while I talk to you. But just before they start the jigsaw, I will take out a few pieces, and put them in my pocket!

There are lots of different kinds of jigsaws, and there are lots of different kinds of schools: some are very big, and are for older children; some are quite small and are for very young children; this one is middle-sized, and is for middle-sized children, like you.

All jigsaws have to be kept in something, so that the pieces don't get lost. You, children, are looked after in our school, so that you don't get lost.

Some of the jigsaw pieces are very easy to fit together. It is easy to see where they go, like the four corner pieces of this one the children are doing now. Some of you children are much easier to look after and teach, than others, but you all belong to our school family, just like the pieces all belong to this jigsaw.

Now, these two children have used all the jigsaw pieces on the table, and now they are stuck; they cannot finish the puzzle. They can't finish it, because some of the pieces are missing. The jigsaw won't be complete until all the pieces are together, in the same way that our school is not complete until all the children are together. If I give these children the pieces from my pocket, they will be able to finish the jigsaw . . . and there it is, completed.

I will take out the smallest piece of the jigsaw puzzle. Do you think the puzzle is any good now? No, it needs all its pieces to be whole and to be useful, just as our school needs all the children, even the smallest, to be a whole school.

Schools and jigsaws need all their pieces, from the biggest to the smallest, to be whole and worthwhile.

This jigsaw is like our school in another way too. At the beginning, when the children started to do the puzzle, all the pieces were separate and loose in their box. Slowly as the puzzle was made, the pieces started to fit together. This week, at the beginning of our new school year, we are all new and separate. We have all gone into new classes; there is new work to do and there are new friends to make. Slowly, as the days go by, I hope we too will start to fit together and work together well.

Prayer
Dear God, please bless our school and help us all to work together and play together, so that our school will be a happy place for us all.

Amen

Hymn
'One more step along the world I go' **C&P**

The first page   *Week 1   Beginnings*

September is the beginning of the school year, and everything is new. Some of you have just started our school, and so everything is very new to you. Many of you have of course been to school before, but there are still many things that are new to you: a new class, a new teacher, new books, new work, new friends.

All of you will have been given new books to work in. Perhaps you have already used the first page. The first page of a new book is always special, isn't it? You sit and you look at its clean whiteness. It makes you want to do your very best work in it. It makes you want to start in a good way.

There was once a man who had worked very hard to become a sea-captain. He had sailed round the world many times on other captains' ships, and now the time had come for him to be given a ship of his own. He felt so proud on his first day as a fully-qualified sea captain, as he stood on the deck of his ship in his smart uniform, welcoming all his crew members aboard. At last all was ready for them to cast off from shore. The crew was on board, the provisions for the voyage were all stowed away, and the cargo they were taking over the sea to foreign countries was safely stowed in the cargo hold. The captain ordered the ship to cast off, and slowly, sedately, serenely, the ship moved out of harbour and into the open sea.

All went well on that first day. The sun shone, the sea was calm, the crew worked hard, and the captain was happy. He walked round and round his ship, checking that all was in order, and seeing that all the crew were working well at their jobs. He spent a good deal of time on the bridge, checking the instruments and making sure the ship was on its right course, travelling at the right speed. All was well.

In the evening, after his dinner the captain went to his cabin to fill in his reports, check on his charts and maps, and write his log. All ships have a ship's log. It is a book in which the captain must write everything of importance to do with the journey. Each day the captain must write details of changes of speed, wind direction and weather conditions, notes of other ships which are seen, and details of the behaviour of the crew.

The problem was, this captain had never written a ship's log before, and he didn't know what he was supposed to write. He sat down at his desk with the big leatherbound book in front of him. It was brand-new, nothing had yet been written in it. The captain stared at the blank, white, empty, first page. His mind was as blank as the page; he had no idea at all what to write. The longer he stared the more worried he became. He knew he must write something, he had to write something every day, but what could he write? He sat and stared and stared and sat. He sat and stared at the empty first page for three hours.

At last, he picked up his pen, and he wrote in his best handwriting 'It has been a calm day', then he put his pen away, closed the book and went to bed.

All the next day, he worried about the log book. He knew he would have to write in it again. He couldn't write the same words as yesterday's entry. All day he wondered what to put. In the evening he sat down at his desk again and was flicking through the pages of the book when a piece of paper fell out. The captain read the paper; on it were written all the things that captains should write in the log book. The captain smiled as he realised how silly yesterday's writing looked. He wondered whether to tear out the page, or to cross out the writing, and do it again, putting down the things he now knew he should write. In the end he decided to leave yesterday's entry exactly as it was, and to write the log book properly from today onwards. After all, it would be cheating if he wrote yesterday's entry today. So the entry stayed on page one of the book, and every time he looked at it, the captain remembered his very first day as a sea captain.

Perhaps you know that schools as well as ships have log books. Our school has a log book in which I write anything of importance or interest to our school. This is our school's log book. All these pages that have already been written on, are of days that have now passed. These empty pages are for the things that will happen in our school during this new school year. I wonder what will be written in it by the end of the year? We must remember to look when we get to the last week of the year.

Prayer
Help us, Lord, to do our best in this new school year.
Help us to do our best work in all our new books.
Help us to set ourselves an example on page one of our school year.
Amen

Hymn
'The ink is black' **C&P**

The parts of the body   *Week 1   Beginnings*
adapted from Aesop

If I were to ask you who belongs to our school I think you would all say that you belong, and that the teachers belong. Today I want you to think of all the other people that help our school every day. Who are they?

Yes, there is the caretaker who looks after our building, the cleaners who keep the school clean and warm, the kitchen ladies who cook our lunches every day, the dinner ladies who look after us at lunch time, the mums who come to school to help in the classroom and the secretary who adds up the register numbers and types the letters. Then there are the people who help sometimes, but not every day; who are they?

There is the school doctor, the nurse, the welfare officer, the heating engineers, the plumber, the joiner and the electrician.

So you see, there is an amazing number of people who all work together to make sure that our school runs smoothly and well. Everyone has a job to do, in the team, and all the jobs are important. If only one of the people didn't do their job properly it would affect the whole school. This reminds me of a story about the parts of the body, who one day didn't work together.

Once upon a time, long long ago, the parts of the body did not work together as well as they do now. They all had a voice and a mind of their own!

Now, on one particular day they all began to complain about the stomach.

'He's so lazy', said the hands. 'We work hard all day, and he does nothing but accept food which we give him. It's just not fair.'

'You're right', said the feet. 'We work hard too; we walk miles every day, mostly getting food for him, yet he does no work.'

'It's true', said the teeth, 'just think of all the work I do, chewing his food, whilst he does no work at all.'

'I think we should stop feeding him', said the eyes. 'He is so lazy he doesn't deserve our help.'

'Agreed', said the other parts of the body; and they all stopped helping.

The brain would not think of food to eat. The feet would not walk to get food. The eyes would not look at food. The hands would not hold a knife and fork, or carry food. The mouth would not open to let food enter. The teeth would not chew food and the tongue and throat would not swallow. The parts of the body felt very pleased with themselves – but not for long. Soon each part began to feel weak and wobbly. The brain felt confused and could hardly think at all. The feet dragged along the ground and the eyes could not focus properly. The hands could not grip or lift anything; the teeth grew loose and began to fall out; the tongue felt rough and the throat was sore.

'What is happening to us?' asked all the parts of the body.

At last the stomach spoke. 'I cannot live without all you parts', it said, 'but now perhaps you realise that you cannot live without me either. You must understand that we each need everyone else. We all need to work together; we each cannot manage without everyone else.'

The parts had learned their lesson, and ever since then have all worked together very well.

Our school is rather like the body in that story. All the parts need to work well together to make our school a happy place. I hope that all the people who come to our school; the children, the teachers, the helpers, the workmen, everyone, will all work together to make our school a happy, successful school.

Prayer

Thank you, God, for all the people who work together
        to make our school the place it is.
Help us to remember that everyone has an important part to play,
        and that everyone needs everyone else.
Help us to be ready to play our part.

Amen

Hymn
'Join with us' **C&P**

The very important man   *Week 2   Small things matter*

Sometimes it is very easy for us to think that small things are not important.
It is easy to forget that small things and small people are as important as
bigger things and bigger people. Sometimes we forget how important little
everyday things are, like pencils, toothbrushes, drawing pins, spoons. Our
lives would be very difficult without those little helpful things. Sometimes
we look down on little animals, and we forget that they are part of the world
and that they matter.

Once upon a time there was a Very Important Man who was always very
busy. He spent all his time going to very important meetings, and seeing
very important people and making very important decisions. When he first
became important the man was quite nice, was helpful and kind to his wife,
his children, and the people who worked for him. But as the man became
used to being important he started to be impatient, cross, bad-tempered
and bossy. He ordered everyone about, he didn't care about their feelings
and he never had time to spend on anyone but himself. He became selfish,
and he thought nobody mattered but him.

One day his wife decided that the time had come to teach him a lesson.
She wrote down on a piece of paper all the little jobs that people did to
make the important man's life easier.
She wrote down:

Paul   – who looked after the car and kept the engine working properly,
Bill   – who cleaned his office, emptied the rubbish bins, cleaned the
              washbasins and toilets,
Sylvia   – who answered the telephone for him and made sure that his
              pencils and paper and scissors and sellotape were all in the
              right place,
and herself – who made his breakfasts and dinners and teas, and ironed his
              shirts and washed his socks.

Then she asked him if all those people's jobs were as important as his job.
'As important as my job?' he shouted. 'Certainly not. How silly. My job
is the most important job in the world. Those other jobs don't matter.'

His wife thought he might say that, so she secretly went to see Paul, Bill
and Sylvia.

The next day the important man got up and went downstairs for his
breakfast.

'I'm sorry,' said his wife, 'there's no breakfast today, I've got more important jobs to do.' The man was astonished and did without his breakfast. He
went outside to get his car. 'I'm sorry,' said Paul, 'I haven't cleaned your

car. It isn't going very well, and it's run out of petrol. I've had more important jobs to do than look after your car.' The man felt very angry and set off to walk to work.

When he arrived at work he walked into his office, and his eyes nearly popped out of his head. The rubbish bin was overflowing, there was dirt everywhere, all his pens, pencils and papers from his desk had disappeared, the telephone was ringing, and two important visitors were sitting in the chaos, waiting to be seen.

'I'm sorry,' said Sylvia from the doorway, 'I can't answer the telephone, I have other important jobs to do.'

'I'm sorry,' shouted Bill from the doorway, 'I haven't had time to tidy up, I've other important things to do.'

At last the man understood. 'I'm sorry,' he said, 'all the jobs you do are important. All the little things in my life are important. I've been too selfish to notice.'

Then he went home to his wife and family and told them he was sorry too. From that day he never forgot that small things, and other people, were just as important as he was.

Prayer

Help us, God, to remember the importance of little everyday things.
Help us never to look down on other people
    and never to think of them as less important than us.
Make us know that everyone is important to you.

Amen

Hymn
'The wise may bring their learning' **C&P**

The Leviathan

Week 2   Small things matter

Strength is not always measured by size. There are times when small people or animals can show greater strength or power than bigger ones. Think of a tiny flea, it can jump many times its own height – a man cannot do that. Think of a leopard; it is not as big as an elephant, but it can run faster. Sometimes tiny animals can be strong by working together in their own community, like bees in a hive, or ants in a hill.

Once upon a time there were three fishermen, who lived on an island. The first fisherman was very old. The second fisherman was middle-aged and was the first fisherman's son. The third fisherman was young and was the first fisherman's grandson.

The three men always went fishing together, every day, in a boat they shared between them. They were honest and fair men. Each day, they took from the sea only the fish they needed to eat, and just enough to sell in the market place to earn a living for their families.

One day the three fishermen were out in their boat, with their nets dangling over the side, when a terrible storm blew up. The sky became dark, great black clouds of mist swirled around the boat and the waves grew tremendous. The black clouds turned into beating rain, and the wind whipped up the waves into crashing foam which drenched the fishermen. Their oars were useless in the fury of the sea, and they were swept far away from the safety of the island shores. Still the storm raged, and they were swept further and further from land.

Eventually the rain stopped, the wind died down and the sea became calm. The frightened men looked around them. There was no land in sight. They had no idea where they were, and no way of finding out. They had no radio in their boat, and no engine, just oars. They did not know which way to row, they did not know where land was.

'What shall we do?' asked the youngest fisherman in a frightened voice.

'We shall surely die', said the middle-aged fisherman.

'We need the help of the Leviathan', said the oldest fisherman.

'Who is he?' asked the others.

'He is the powerful, sea-monster of the deep. My own grandfather used to tell me of him', said the old man. 'Many a sea yarn he has told me of the Leviathan. He would be able to help three honest fishermen.'

'Then call for him', said the youngest, and he began to shout at the sea. 'Leviathan, come and help us. Please help us get home.'

Suddenly there was a plop in the water at the side of the ship, and a fish poked up its head.

'What do you want?' asked the fish.

'We want the sea-monster to help us get home', said the fishermen.

'I'll find him', said the fish, and he disappeared beneath the water again.

For several minutes all was still, and the three men waited fearfully, wondering what the sea-monster would be like. Perhaps it would be huge and frightening, perhaps it would emerge from the sea and make a wave that would capsize their boat. Perhaps the Leviathan would not be friendly towards them, and they dared not think what would happen then.

While they were looking and waiting, a small silver fish swam up to the boat and said, 'Are you looking for me?'

'For you?' said the men. 'Oh no! We're looking for the sea-monster, the Leviathan.'

'I am the Leviathan', said the fish.

'You?' said the men in astonishment. 'But you can't help us get back to land. You are small. We were expecting a monster.'

'Leviathan means someone with power, not just size', said the fish. 'Now, do you need my help?'

'Yes, please', said the men.

'Then throw one end of your nets into the sea', said the fish, 'and hold on tight!'

The men did as they were told, and watched in amazement as sea creatures of all shapes and sizes swam towards the boat and took hold of the nets. At a command by the Leviathan, they all began to swim in the same direction, pulling the boat behind them, and soon the shape of the island came into view. The sea creatures swam on until the boat was only a little way from land, then they all let go of the nets and turned back to the open sea. The Leviathan was last to leave.

'Thank you', called the fishermen. 'You are the smallest 'monster' we've ever met, but you are surely the strongest.'

The Leviathan waved its tail at them and disappeared into the waves.

The fish in the story was small, but could organise many other creatures to do something useful. The other creatures respected the fish, and trusted him, and did what he wanted them to do. The strength of the fish was not in his size, but in his ability. We do not need to be big to be helpful and to work together like the fish.

Prayer

Dear God, please help us all to put our strengths together
and do our share of helping in our school and homes.
Help us to remember that everyone, big or small, is important.

Amen

Hymn
'God knows me' **C&P**

Robert the Bruce   *Week 2   Small things matter*

Small people, animals or objects cannot always help us to do things, because of their small size, but sometimes they can inspire us; they can give us an idea, and so help us in that way. Today's story is about a spider who wasn't able to help the man by actually doing anything for him, but he did help in another way.

The man was a king. His name was King Robert the Bruce of Scotland. His army had been involved in many battles with the English army, and at each battle, King Robert was driven further back. He was now in danger of losing much of his land. His army was tired, weary and could not see the point in carrying on fighting, when they lost all the time.

King Robert, feeling that everything was hopeless, hid for a while in a hut on the moors. The hut was poor and shabby; little more than a shed. King Robert sat down on a rickety wooden chair, leaned his elbows on an old wooden table, put his head in his hands, and thought.

'What are we to do?' he sighed. 'It's hopeless. We might as well give ourselves up and let the English army take what it wants.'

Just at that moment Robert noticed, out of the corner of his eye, a spider dangling on a silken thread from one of the beams in the roof. He lifted his head and watched the spider. It seemed to be trying to swing from side to side.* Robert watched more closely. The spider was trying to swing across to another wooden beam. It was trying to reach the second beam so that it could fasten its silken thread and make a web. Across the space it swung, but missed the beam and swung back to where it started. It tried again, across the space . . . but missed and went back to where it started. Again it tried, a harder swing this time, with more effort, across the space . . . but once again it missed the beam and went back to where it started.

Again and again the spider tried to attach its thread to the beam, again and again it missed. Still Robert watched. The spider swung again . . . and managed this time to reach the beam. Quickly it fastened the thread to the wood and hurried back to fasten it to a lower beam as well. In no time now the spider had built the foundations of its web, and was able to finish it.

Robert sat and watched, and slowly an idea came to him.

'I am like that spider', he said. 'I have tried and tried to do something. I have tried to win a battle to save my land and my country; but unlike the spider, I have given up because I've not succeeded. The spider did not give up, he kept on trying until he fastened his thread to the beam. The spider has told me, "If at first you don't succeed, try, try, try, again." I will try again. I will not give up.'

Robert the Bruce, now full of enthusiasm again, went out of his hiding place, summoned his army, and went on to win back his land from the English.

We, I hope, are not involved in battles or fights, but we can learn from the spider in Robert's story. If we find something hard to do, we can keep on trying. If we try hard, hopefully, we will succeed.

Remember, if at first you don't succeed, try, try, try again.

Prayer

Thank you, God, for all small living things;
       for insects, birds and tiny creatures.
Help us never to despise small animals.
Help us to know that sometimes small animals can help us.

Amen

Hymn
'All things bright and beautiful' **C&P**

I illustrated this story with the simple visual aid of a cut-out cardboard spider, blu-tacked to a piece of chalk. As the story unfolded I moved the spider (and chalk) like a pendulum from side to side of a free-standing blackboard (black paper pinned to the wall would do). The 'swings' increased in width until, to represent the successful 'swing', the chalk reached the opposite side of the blackboard. Thus the first silken thread of the web was drawn on to the board. If care is then taken to draw the web correctly, the children also learn the formation of a common spider's web.

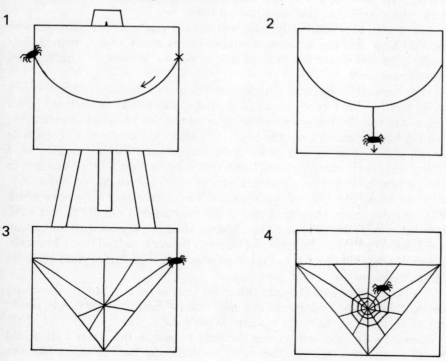

Mrs Do-unto-others   *Week 3*

Do unto others as you would have them do unto you

There is a saying which goes 'Do unto others as you would have them do
unto you.' It means treat other people as you hope they will treat you. If
you want people to be kind to you, be kind to them. If you want someone
to be friendly to you, be friendly to them. If you want people to be fair to
you, then be fair to them. If everyone did this, we would have a happy
world. We can make sure we have a happy school, by treating people as we
would like them to treat us. Many of you will have already found out for
yourselves that if you are nice to your friends, they are usually nice to you,
but if you are cross and bad-tempered, or if you cheat or play unfairly they
are not likely to be very friendly towards you.

Mrs Do-unto-others knew that. She was an old lady who had lived in the
street for as long as anyone could remember. No-one knew what her real
name was. Everyone called her Mrs Do-unto-others, because she was always
saying: 'Do unto others as you would have them do unto you.' She meant
treat other people as you want them to treat you.

She was a very kind lady. She was always ready to help anyone who
needed help, and she never said unkind things about anyone behind their
backs. She was never too busy to talk to people, no matter whether they
were six or sixty.

One summer, some new people came to live in the street. They were a
noisy family, with lots of cats and dogs and children. The mother and father
seemed to spend a lot of time shouting at all the cats and dogs and children,
but neither the animals nor the boys and girls took much notice. The whole
family didn't seem to care much about anyone else as long as they were
doing what they wanted to do. The father used to light a lot of bonfires in
the garden; he didn't care whether anyone's clean washing was out to dry,
or if the smoke blew into people's houses. The mother used to tip her rubbish
bin over the fence; she didn't care if the tin cans and the old papers went
into other people's gardens. The children used to play football and break
windows. They used to trample on people's flower beds and break branches
off their trees. They used to play loud music on their radios, and wake up
all the babies when they'd gone to bed.

Every day when Mrs Do-unto-others met any of the new family, she would
say to them, 'Good Morning! Do unto others!' and the new family would
say to themselves, 'Silly old woman. What's she saying?'

Soon Mrs Do-unto-others was the only person in the street who would
speak to the new family. The other mothers and fathers didn't like the
family, so they simply tried to take no notice of them. The other children

didn't like playing with the new children, because they played rough games, and usually ended up getting into trouble.

One day there was an accident in the new family's house. The chip pan caught fire, and before anyone had time to do anything about it the curtains and the kitchen had caught fire. The whole family rushed out into the garden, and luckily no-one was hurt. 'Help', shouted the mother and father, 'Get the fire brigade.'

Mrs Do-unto-others telephoned for the fire engine, and in a few minutes it had arrived and the fire was put out. But the kitchen was in a terrible mess. The walls were black with smoke, the curtains were in tatters, the cupboards were burnt and blistered and the floor was deep in water from the fire engine's hosepipes.

'Well, you can't use this kitchen until you have it repaired', said Mrs Do-unto-others. 'We'll help, won't we, everyone?' And much to the new family's surprise, everyone said yes.

Mrs Robinson took the two eldest children to her house for tea; Mrs Smith took the three youngest to her house, and said they could sleep there for the night. Mrs Brown said she would do all the new family's washing in her washing machine, until the kitchen was repaired. Mr Robinson, Mr Jones and Mr Brown said they would help to take out the damaged kitchen cupboards and put in some new ones.

'Why is everyone being so nice to us?' asked the new family.

'Do unto others', said Mrs Do-unto-others. 'We believe that you should treat other people as you hope they will treat you. If any of us had an accident in our house, we would hope that people would help us; and so when it happened to you, we knew we had to do something.'

'Thank you', said the new family.

From that day on, the new family was much more thoughtful to the neighbours, and they tried hard to 'do unto others', just as Mrs Do-unto-others had shown them.

Doing to others what you want them to do to you really does work. You can try this experiment to prove it. Smile at someone and see what happens. Frown, or look crossly at someone and see what happens.*

You will see that if you have a happy smiling face, you will mostly have faces smiling back at you, but if you look cross and grumpy, people will be cross and grumpy back.

Prayer

Dear God, help us to treat other people as we hope they will treat us.

Help us to remember that a smile usually makes another smile.

Amen

Hymn
'Cross over the road' **C&P**

*We tried the experiment in the assembly by showing two faces drawn on card, and mounted, puppet-fashion, on sticks. The smiling face, held first, caused smiles from the children; the frowning (sad) face caused no smiles.

The fox and the stork   Week 3   Do unto others . . .
adapted from Aesop

If you are kind, friendly and helpful to people, it usually makes those people want to be kind, friendly and helpful to you. How do you think people will behave towards you if you are nasty, or mean, selfish or unkind? Yes, I'm afraid it usually makes them want to behave in a similar way back to you!

Today I have a story about a fox and a stork. The actions of the fox made the stork want to get her own back. Let's listen to what happened.

A fox and a stork lived quite near each other in the wood, but I'm sorry to say, were not the best of friends. One day the fox decided to play an unkind trick on the stork. He went to the stork's house and said, 'Would you like to come and have dinner at my house tomorrow?'

The stork thought it very strange that the fox should be inviting her to dinner, but she thought, 'Perhaps the fox is really trying to be friendly. I don't want to upset him, if that's what he's doing. I must show him that I'm trying to be friendly too.'

'Yes', she said, 'I would very much like to have dinner at your house.'

'Good', said the fox. 'Don't be late, we don't want the soup to go cold, do we?' and he laughed in a mysterious way.

The next day the stork went to the fox's house. 'Ah, hello', he said. 'Come in and sit down. The soup is almost ready.'*

The stork sat down at the table, and in a few moments the fox brought a wide, shallow dish of watery soup, which he put on the table between them.

'In my part of the wood,' said the fox, 'we usually share a dish. You don't mind, do you?'

'Of course not', answered the stork, but she looked unhappily at the low, flat dish.

The fox started to drink the soup noisily, lapping it up easily with his tongue. The stork, however, hardly managed to have any soup at all. She put the tip of her long, thin beak into the soup dish, but the dish was far too shallow for her to be able to drink any of the soup. She was much too polite to compain to the fox, and anyway she didn't want to upset him. The fox greedily and noisily drank all the soup, whilst she sat there looking unhappy and feeling hungry. When she set off home, after dinner, she heard the fox laughing at her, and knew that he had played the trick on purpose.

'He thinks he's got the better of me,' said the stork to herself, 'but I'll show him.'

The next day, the stork went to the fox's house and knocked on his door. He was very surprised to see her.

'You were so kind to me yesterday, fox,' she said, 'that I would like to repay your kindness and invite you to come and have dinner at my house tomorrow.'

The fox was astonished, but he didn't want to show the stork that he was surprised.

'Thank you, stork', he said. 'I would love to come to dinner tomorrow.'

'Don't be late, will you?' she said. 'I don't want the soup to go cold!' And she smiled at the fox, as she turned to go home.

'If I didn't know her better, I would think that she was up to something', thought the fox.

The following day the fox arrived at the stork's house. He hadn't eaten anything all day and was really looking forward to his dinner. The stork asked him to sit at the table and said the soup would not be long before it was ready.

A few minutes later the stork put the tallest jug the fox had ever seen, in the middle of the table. The jug was full of delicious, steaming soup, but the fox's face fell when he realised that he was expected to share the jug with the stork. The jug was so tall, and had such a narrow opening at the top, that he couldn't possibly drink out of it.

'In my part of the wood,' said the stork, 'we also usually share a dish, and I always use this jug. You don't mind sharing, do you?' and she daintily dipped her long thin beak into the tall jug, and drank the soup easily. The fox could not get his nose into the jug at all; he could only lick the soup drops that dribbled over the edge of the jug. He was hungry and angry; but he couldn't complain, because of course, he had played exactly the same trick on the stork two days earlier.

'In future,' he thought, 'I'll treat others as I want them to treat me!'

It was unkind of the stork to play the same nasty trick on the fox, because after all, two wrongs do not make a right; but it certainly taught the fox a lesson.

Prayer

> Dear God, please help us to think about other people.
> Help us to be considerate towards other people.
> Help us to treat other people as we hope they will treat us.
>
> *Amen*

Hymn
'When I needed a neighbour' **C&P**

*I illustrated this story by having a small table and tablecloth at the front of the hall, with a chair positioned at each side. As the story unfolded, I brought to the table a flat, wide soup dish, and a tall, narrow-necked pitcher (vase).

The boy who complained   Week 3   Do unto others . . .

Sometimes, when someone does something wrong or hurtful to you, it is necessary for you to tell your teacher, or your mum or dad if you're at home. In our school, if someone annoys you a lot, or fights with you, we ask you to tell the teacher on duty, so that the problem can be sorted out, and so that no-one gets hurt or upset. But sometimes it is hard to decide whether to tell or not. If someone is constantly upsetting you, then you need to tell, but of course you don't want to be running telling tales every few minutes.

I once knew a boy who was always telling tales. The trouble was that most of the time there was no need to tell. Most of the time the boy was telling tales in order to try and get other people into trouble.

On one particular day, the boy never stopped telling tales about his friends. As soon as the children went out onto the playground, he began.

'John's hitting me', he said to the teacher, when in fact John had done no such thing.

'Imran's pushed me over', he said, when Imran had accidentally bumped into him while they had been playing a game.

'Aisha's pulling faces at me', he said a few minutes later. It was true, she was pulling faces but only because he was being a nuisance to her; and there was really no need for him to make a fuss to the teacher about it.

'Sarah's kicked me', he said a few minutes later. Sarah had accidentally kicked him whilst they were playing football. She hadn't kicked him on purpose, and she did take the trouble to say she was sorry to the boy.

The boy continued for almost the entire playtime, going to the teacher, and complaining about various children. By the end of playtime the teacher was tired of listening to the complaints, and the rest of the children were quite cross and indignant about it, because they had not deliberately set out to annoy or hurt the boy.

Just before the end of playtime, the teacher took the boy quietly on one side, just as he was about to make yet another complaint about someone else.

'Look', she said. 'Have *you* never done anything wrong? Have *you* never accidentally knocked into someone, or accidentally kicked someone while you've been playing football? Have *you* never pulled a face at anyone, or been unfriendly in any other way?'

'Well . . . ' said the boy, 'sometimes.'

'And did you like it when people went to tell about you?' she asked.

'No . . . ' said the boy, 'but . . . '

'But nothing!' went on the teacher. 'Would you want to be friends with someone who was always telling tales about you?'

'No', said the boy.

'Then just think about it', said the teacher. 'Try to treat your friends in the same way that you want them to treat you. Now off you go, it's nearly in–time!'

The next playtime, the same teacher noticed that the boy didn't come to her with complaints nearly as often as he had done during the morning playtime. And curiously enough, he seemed to be having a much happier playtime!

This story is rather like a story in the Bible.

A woman had done something wrong, and the normal punishment in those days, for many crimes, was that the wrong-doer should be stoned to death. A group of people were standing round ready to throw the stones at the woman, and Jesus came by and said, 'If there is one of you here, who has never done anything wrong, then you throw the first stone.'

Of course there was no-one who had *never* done anything wrong, because everyone at some time or another has done something they should not have done. So no-one could throw the first stone. Slowly everyone went away, leaving the woman alone, to go back to her home.

Jesus taught people to care for others, and to treat other people as we would like to be treated.

Let us, in our school, care for each other; look after each other, and treat each other as we want to be treated.

Prayer

Dear God, help us to make our school a caring school.

Help us to look after each other and to show kindness to each other.

Help us to treat our friends as we hope they will treat us.

Amen

Hymn

'The family of man' **C&P**

All for the want of a horse-shoe nail   *Week 4   Doing jobs well*

This week in school we had a 'hitch' with the jobs. It all started off in a very small way. Some children who were going to give out the registers, forgot to come at the right time, and went into the playground instead. When they at last remembered to come in to do their job, it was nearly in–time, and because they were late the children did the job carelessly, in a hurry. As a result of that, class 2 were given class 7's register, class 3 got class 5's, class 6 got class 1's, and all the registers ended up in a muddle. By the time they were all sorted out again everyone was late starting the day. Everyone was late into assembly, and then late into their classrooms for lessons. Somehow those lost minutes were never found, and the whole day went wrong. And all that happened because a small job wasn't done properly.

There is a nursery rhyme about something small – you might know it.

> For want of a nail, the shoe was lost;
> For want of a shoe, the horse was lost;
> For want of a horse, the rider was lost;
> For want of a rider, the battle was lost;
> For want of a battle, the kingdom was lost;
> And all for the want of a horse-shoe nail.

The story of that nursery rhyme happened a long long time ago. There was a rich and famous king called King Sebastian who had a huge kingdom and a strong army to defend that kingdom.

One day King Arroganté from the country next door gathered his army together and set off to have a battle with King Sebastian, because he wanted to take King Sebastian's kingdom.

King Sebastian's messengers came hurrying to the palace with news of the advancing army.

'We must prepare for battle', they said. 'King Arroganté's army is on its way.'

'Prepare for battle', announced the King. 'Prepare well, we must be ready for the attack.'

All the King's men went away to do their jobs in readiness for the battle.

The Royal Silversmith polished and sharpened all the silver swords, and checked the straps and handles on the silver shields.

The Royal Armourer checked and cleaned all the soldiers' armour. He checked the helmets, the chain mail and the breastplates.

The Royal Flagbearers polished their poles and furled their flags.

The Saddlers checked the saddles and harness, bridles and reins, to see that all was safe and secure.

The Royal Blacksmith looked at the horses' shoes to see that they were firm and clean. First he looked at the shoes of the soldiers' horses, then he looked at the shoes of the King's horse. But unfortunately he was not a very careful worker, and he was sometimes lazy. By the time he had checked the soldiers' horses' shoes, he was feeling tired, so when he found a loose nail in one of the King's horse's shoes, he said to himself, 'Well, I'm too tired to put on a new horse shoe now. Anyway it won't matter, it's only one little nail in one little horse shoe of one little horse. That's not going to make any difference to the army.' And he went to bed.

The next morning the army gathered together outside the castle. The soldiers in their armour were mounted on their horses. The King, on his horse, waited at the front of the army. The flagbearers were standing by.

Suddenly, King Arroganté's army appeared in the distance.

'Charge!' ordered King Sebastian. Straightaway the whole army burst into life. With flags waving and trumpets sounding the soldiers spurred their horses on, galloping over the field. On and on, faster and faster they galloped, with the King in the lead. Towards them galloped King Arroganté's army.

But the loose nail, in the King's horse's shoes was still loose! As the horse galloped over the grass the nail became looser, and then dropped out. The horse shoe became loose, and then it dropped off, and when that happened the horse stumbled, and fell. The King fell into a heap on the grass. The first line of soldiers fell over the King. The second line of soldiers fell over the first line, and the third line fell over the second line. Soon the whole army was in an enormous heap on the ground. Whilst it was picking itself up and dusting itself down, King Arroganté's army surrounded the field and the castle, and claimed the Kingdom.

And so it was that King Sebastian lost his battle, and his Kingdom: all because a lazy blacksmith thought one small nail didn't matter.

The world now knows that it did.

Lots of children in our school do jobs to help. Some of those jobs are difficult and important. Some of those jobs are easy and quite small, but they are still important. Let's make sure that when we do a job, we do it as well as we can, whether it is a big or a small job.

Prayer

Dear God, help us to remember that small jobs are important.
Small jobs in school are important.
Small jobs done properly can make big jobs go well.
Help us to be helpful.

Amen

Hymn

'When a knight won his spurs' **C&P**

The donkey and the horse
adapted from Aesop

Sometimes when you are asked to do a job to help, at home or school, you don't really want to help at that time. Perhaps you are in the middle of doing something else, or perhaps you want to go out to play with your friends. Sometimes, when you are asked to do something, you think – 'Do I have to?' Well, the answer to that, usually is yes, because it is very important for everyone to do their fair share of the work. It wouldn't be fair if one person in your family did *all* the work, and no one else ever did anything to help. It wouldn't be fair in your class if one person always did *all* the tidying up, and no-one else ever helped to put anything away.

There was once a man who owned a donkey and a horse. The donkey was small, grey, hardworking and friendly. The horse was big, black, lazy and very proud. Every week the man went to market to sell vegetables, and every week he took the donkey and the horse with him. The donkey had to carry all the sacks of vegetables; the carrots, potatoes, cabbages, swedes and turnips. He had to carry the man's bags, in case he wanted to stay in the town overnight; and he had to carry any parcels and packages that the man wanted to take with him. In fact, the donkey had to carry everything, except the man; the horse carried him!

One day, there seemed to be more to carry than usual. There were strings of onions, and bunches of radishes, bags of beetroot and bundles of leeks, as well as all the usual sacks of vegetables. The poor donkey was absolutely laden, and could hardly walk. He was not feeling very well that day, anyway.

They hadn't gone very far when the donkey said to the horse, 'I don't think I can go much further. I feel so tired, and all the vegetables are so heavy today. Please will you help me to carry something, horse? If you share the load, I think I can manage.'

'Me?' said the horse. 'You expect me to carry vegetables? I can't do that. I am a fine horse! I am a thoroughbred! I carry the master! I am not a beast of burden like you, I cannot be expected to carry vegetables. That is your job, get on with it.'

And with that, the horse tossed his fine, proud head, and trotted on in front, with the man on his back.

The poor, tired, donkey, staggered a few more steps, and then his legs gave way under all the weight he was carrying, and he sank to the ground in a heap.

The man turned round, saw the donkey lying still on the ground, and hurried back to where he lay.

'Oh dear', he said. 'Perhaps I gave him too much to carry, there was rather a lot this week. Never mind, the horse is strong, he can manage it all.'

'Me?' gasped the horse. 'I am to carry everything?'

'You are strong enough', said the man. 'Anyway, we can't leave the donkey and all the vegetables here, so you'll have to help.'

Without more ado, the man loaded all the sacks and bundles of vegetables onto the horse's back. Then he loaded on the bags, parcels and packages. Then, last of all, very gently, the man lifted the donkey from the ground and carefully put him across the horse's back as well. By now the donkey was feeling a little better.

'In future', said the man, 'you will both share the load, then it will be fair.'

'I wish I'd done my fair share earlier,' thought the horse, 'then I wouldn't be carrying everything now.'

The horse learned the hard way, that it's best to share the work. Unfortunately, because he didn't do his share in the first place, he ended up having to do *all* the work.

We should try to remember that story, and try to do our share of the work; or one day we may be like the horse, and have to do everyone else's share as well as our own!

Prayer

Dear God, please teach us all, whether big or small,
     to do our share of helping.
Teach us to offer our help whenever we can;
teach us not to expect other people to do our share;
teach us to be helpful and considerate towards everyone.

Amen

Hymn
'Cross over the road' **C&P**

The mouse, the frog and the little red hen   *Week 4   Doing jobs well*
traditional

In our last assembly, we heard of a horse and a donkey, who didn't share a job fairly or equally. At the end of the story, the horse, who up until then had done no work, had to do it all. Today I am going to read you, not a story, but a poem, about someone else who did *all* the work. Listen carefully.

Once a mouse, a frog and a little red hen
Together kept a house;
The frog was the laziest of frogs
And lazier still was the mouse.

So the work all fell on the little red hen,
Who had to get the wood,
And build the fires, and scrub, and cook,
And sometimes hunt the food.

One day as she went scratching round,
She found a bag of rye.
She said, 'Now, who will make some bread?'
The lazy mouse said, 'Not I!'

'Nor I', croaked the frog as he dozed in the shade.
The hen made no reply,
But flew around with a bowl and a spoon,
And mixed and stirred the rye.

'Who'll make the fire to bake the bread?'
The mouse said again, 'Not I!'
And hardly opened his sleepy eye
The frog made the same reply.

The little red hen said never a word,
But a great big fire she made,
And while the bread was baking brown,
'Who'll set the table?' she said.

'Not I', said the sleepy frog with a yawn;
'Not I', said the mouse again.
So the table she set, and the bread she put on,
'Who'll eat the bread?' said the hen.

'I will', cried the frog. 'And I will', said the mouse
As nearer the table they drew.
'Oh no you won't!' said the little red hen,
And away with the loaf she flew.

The hen kept all the loaf for herself, because she was the one who did all the work. Perhaps you think that's fair, or perhaps you think that she should have shared it with the others, even though they didn't do their share of the work.

That poem is rather like the story of the lady who bought an apple tree one day from the market. She brought it home, carefully planted it, and watered it whenever the weather was dry. No-one helped her to look after the little apple tree. Her husband and her four children were always too busy doing something else.

In the autumn, the small apple tree produced just ten apples. 'Just enough for a pie', said the lady. No-one wanted to help her pick the apples, or peel the apples or make the pastry. So the lady picked them, peeled them, made the pastry, cut up the apples, put them in the pie, put the crust on, and baked the pie. Soon it was ready; golden brown steaming and juicy, with a lovely crisp sugary, crunchy crust.

'Who would like a piece of apple pie?' she said, and of course everyone in her family said they wanted a piece.

The story does not tell us whether the lady gave her family a piece of pie each, or whether, like the little red hen, she ate it all herself. What do you think?

Who thinks she ate it herself?

Who thinks she shared it out?

I think that perhaps she shared it with the family, because she was kind and unselfish, but I hope that next time, her family will help her. I hope you don't leave your Mum to do all the work at your house, without ever bothering to help, and I hope you don't leave one person to do all the tidying up in your classroom, without bothering to help.

Prayer

Dear God, let us be ready to give, as well as to take.
Let us be ready to help, as well as to be helped.
Make us ready to do our share of helping at home and at school.

Amen

Hymn
'The family of man' **C&P**

The birthday present

Week 5   Books

Books are important in school. We have lots of different kinds of books in our school: books to write in, books to work from, story books, poetry books and books which give us information and tell us facts. I think if you looked in the houses of all our teachers, you would see lots of books. You have probably got lots of books in your houses as well. Books can be good friends, they can amuse us, inform us, teach us; they can make us laugh or cry; they can give us something to do if we're bored, they can help us to know about other people's thoughts and ideas. I like books, and have a lot of books at home, some of them I've had since I was quite small.

Today's story is about a teacher, but the story happened when she was just eight years old. Every Saturday the girl and her mum went shopping. They went each week to the butcher's, the grocer's, the greengrocer's and the baker's shop, and on the way they always passed the bookshop. Each week the little girl would run to the bookshop window, press her nose against the glass and gaze inside at all the lovely books on display.

Sometimes, if they were not in too much of a hurry, the girl and her mum used to go inside and look at the books on the shelves inside the shop. Sometimes, especially at birthdays and Christmas time, the girl would be able to choose a book to buy.

One day the girl ran to the window and looked inside. There, in the middle of the window she saw a book she would very much like to have. It was quite a large book, and she could see that it had beautiful pictures inside, as well as quite a lot of writing. She looked at the price ticket and saw that it was quite expensive. She was sure that her mum would not be able to afford to buy it for her.

Her mum came then, and stood next to her at the window. 'Can we go in, mum, and look at that book?' said the girl. They went inside, and the book seemed even better when she held it and turned its pages.

'Well!' said her mum, 'I'm afaid I can't afford to buy it for you. Why don't you save up your pocket money, and perhaps with that, and any birthday money you might get for your birthday next month, you may be able to buy it for yourself?'

'That's a good idea. I'll do that', said the girl. That week she didn't spend any of her pocket money on sweets or a comic, as she usually did, but she saved it all. The next week when she looked in the bookshop window, she knew that soon she would be able to buy the book. Each week she saved all her pocket money, and each week she went to look at the bookshop window to check that the book was still there. How awful it would be if it were sold to someone else whilst she was saving up for it. A few days before her birthday, an envelope arrived through the post from her Auntie Dorothy. The envelope contained a card and £1. At last she had enough to buy the book. She asked her mum if she could go to the shop, and she set off at a run. She arrived breathless and panting and peered in through the window. At first, because of her steamy breath on the window she couldn't see the book clearly . . . then she realised she couldn't see her book at all . . . it was gone. The disappointment was dreadful. She felt empty. Slowly, she went into the shop and asked the assistant for the book.

'I'm sorry. That was the only copy I had, and I sold it this morning to a girl a bit older than you', said the assistant.

The girl walked home. She could, she supposed, have chosen another book, but it wouldn't be the same. She really did want the book that she had seen in the window.

In three more days it was her birthday; she was woken by her sister coming into her bedroom. 'Happy Birthday. I've got you a present. I hope you'll like it.' The girl sat up in bed and took the oblong shaped package. She pulled off the coloured string and the wrapping paper, and inside was the book she had wanted so much.

The girl is now grown up, and is a teacher, but she still has the book that was given to her all those years ago. She must have looked after her things, and taken care of them. I hope you look after your books. If you do, you may be able to give them to your own children when you are grown up.

Prayer
Thank you, God, for books.
Thank you for bookshops and libraries.
Thank you for the pleasure that books can bring us.
Help us to look after our books, and treat them well,
     so that they will last a long time.

Amen

Hymn
'Thank you, Lord' **C&P**
– adding a verse 'Thank you, Lord, for books to read'

Books in the time capsule
        Week 5   Books

I wonder what you think this is, (clay tablet) or this (paper scroll).* Yes, this is a clay block or tablet, and this is a roll of paper which we call a scroll. You are right . . . but there is another answer which no-one has given me. These items are both books! Scratched into the clay tablet, are picture words, and if I open up the scroll, you will see words written inside. Books haven't always looked the way they look today.

Let's pretend that we have a time capsule. A time capsule like Dr. Who's, that can move to anywhere in time; a time capsule that can take us back as far in time as we want to travel; a time capsule in which we can sit, and look out on times gone by.

We climb into our time capsule and sit down. There is a huge panel with knobs and dials in front of us. We press the knobs and turn the dials to take us back through time. We travel back, 1000, 2000, 3000, 4000, 5000 years. The pictures through our windows are blurred and hazy, then our time capsule stops and the picture clears. There are Egyptian children, sitting cross legged on the sand in the sunshine, with their teacher standing nearby. These children are rich children; poor children do not have teachers. The children are writing with sticks on blocks of damp clay. They are writing in pictures called hieroglyphics. These clay tablets are the only 'books' they have. They write for their teacher on the tablets and the teacher writes for the children on the tablets. If they want to save their writing they leave the clay tablets out in the sun to harden and dry. One boy drops his clay tablet, and it smashes on the ground into lots of small pieces! I wonder if he will get into trouble.

We climb back in our time capsule and travel forward, 5000, 4000, 3000 years ago. The time capsule stops again, we look through the window. The picture, hazy and blurred at first, clears again. This time we look out and see that we are in Rome in Italy.

Some important men called scribes are sitting round a table. They are writing, but they are not writing on clay tablets, nor on books as we know them. They are writing on pieces of paper made out of reeds which grow by the River Nile in Egypt. The reeds have been gathered together, then crushed, then pressed out to make a kind of paper called papyrus. When the men have finished writing out the pages of the story they are copying, the pages will be fastened together sideways in a long strip. Each end will be glued to a stick, and the sticks will be rolled up to make a scroll, rather like the one I showed you at the beginning of assembly.

One day there is bad news for the scribes of Rome. The people in Egypt who make the papyrus, refuse to send it out of the country. The Roman scribes have no paper to write on. They cannot make their own because the papyrus reeds do not grow in their country. They have to find a new way of making paper. They try lots of experiments, and at last they find a way of making a new kind of paper. They use animal skins: animal skins stretched very thinly, then washed and stretched, washed and stretched, until they become as thin as paper. This new paper is called parchment. Then the scribes discover that the new paper is even more useful than the old paper. The old papyrus will not fold, it cracks and breaks, but the new parchment will fold, and it is much stronger. It can be folded and cut into pages, and the pages can be stitched together to make a book. Now the scribes write on the pages, pages of parchment, and the parchment is stitched together to make a book. The book does not have covers like our school books, but it is now book-shaped, not a scroll or a tablet.

We have one more visit to make in our time capsule: back in our seat; turn the dials and press the knobs; we move forward again, fast, another 1000 years. Now it is 2000 years ago. Another 1000 years forward, then another 500 years, until it is only 500 years ago in Germany. The capsule stops, we see through the window a man. But he is not writing, or reading, he is fitting tiny pieces of metal together. The small pieces of metal have back-to-front letters on them, and they move when a lever is pressed. The man is inventing a printing machine. He tries it out. He puts ink on to the metal letters. He fits a piece of paper behind the metal letters and he presses the levers. At first there is a blot and a blob and then it works. The first printing maching is printing pages. Now many books can be made at the same time. Many more people can have books, and read books. There have never been so many books in the world.

And now back in our time capsule, programme it to return to today. We have beautiful books like these on my table. You don't have to own the books, you can look at them in the school library, or the public library, or in your class library.

I wonder what the books of the future will be like. Wouldn't it be exciting if we could climb inside our time capsule and travel forwards instead of backwards; I wonder what we would see?

Prayer
> Thank you, God, for all our books.
> Thank you for all the inventions in the past,
>> which have helped to make our books as they are today.
> Thank you for schools and teachers,
>> who help us to learn to read.
>
> *Amen*

Hymn
'The ink is black' **C&P**

I had various colourful, attractive children's books on display on the table at the front of the hall. I also had prepared a very simplified scroll, with writing inside, so the children could see how one worked, and a basic clay tablet with indented, homemade hieroglyphics.

Don't judge a book by its cover
adapted from Aesop

Week 5   Books

During the introduction to this assembly we examined six or so books, lent by teaching staff, from their own childhood. We commented on the appearance of the books, their condition, the lack of colour illustrations etc. in the oldest books, as well as making comment upon the actual book content and story plot. The children made guesses at each book's rightful owner. If no staff childhood books are forthcoming, it would be possible to substitute the children's favourite books, and have them bring them prior to the assembly, (and then display them all and select a few of the most suitable for comment). Similarly it would be easy to choose one class's favourite books from their library corner, or simply choose a small selection of favourite books from the school library. From our collection we chose one favourite story to retell.

Earlier this week I told you the story of a girl who wanted a book very badly, and was given it for her birthday. I also told you that the girl, now a teacher, still has that book. Since telling you that story I have discovered that quite a number of our teachers have books that they were given as children, and those teachers have lent me their books to show you. You may be able to guess which book belongs to which teacher.

It is good sometimes, whether you are a child or a grown-up, to read a story just because you enjoy it. One of my favourite stories is Aesop's fable of the lion and the mouse.

Once upon a time a lion was snoozing in the afternoon sun. A tiny mouse woke him by running across his paw. The lion was just about to raise his paw and squash the mouse, when the mouse spoke. 'Please don't hurt me, mighty lion. If you help me by letting me go, I may be able to help you one day.'

'You,' roared the lion, 'help me? The nerve! The cheek! The sheer audacity! As if you, a little nothing, could possibly help me, the king of all beasts. Yes, I'll let you go. You deserve to go for your impudence. But as for helping me . . . ' and the lion roared again as the mouse scampered away.

Several days later, the mouse was scurrying amongst the undergrowth when she heard the Lion's thunderous roar again. 'That sounds like my lion', she thought. Cautiously, she edged nearer, and there, to her amazement was her lion, trapped in an enormous net, put down by human hunters. The more the lion struggled and roared, the more entangled he became. He was becoming wilder with anger and frustration.

'I can help you', murmured the mouse. 'You', roared the lion. 'You!' he repeated softly as he recognized her.

'Stay still', she ordered as she climbed onto the net and began to gnaw and nibble at the rope. Soon she had made a hole big enough to let the lion's paws and front legs through, then his proud head and mane were free, and finally his body emerged from the rope netting. He stretched and shook himself.

'Thank you, mouse', he said. 'I shall never again judge someone by what they look like. You are much stronger, and more useful than you look. Thank you again.'

'It's a pleasure,' she said as she scampered off, 'one good turn deserves another.'

That story reminds me of the saying 'Never judge a book by its cover'. In the same way that the lion couldn't judge the mouse's helpfulness just by looking at her, we can't tell what book will be like just by looking at its cover. We need to look inside and to read it, to see what it's really like.

Prayer
>   Dear God, thank you for all our books.
>   Thank you for stories to read and enjoy.
>   Thank you for the authors who write the stories,
>   and for the publishers and printers who turn the stories into books.
>
> *Amen*

Hymn
'The Lord's Prayer' **C&P**

The African boy   *Week 6   Harvest*

Today I want to introduce you to this boy.* I want you to get to know him.

He lives in a country called Ethiopia which is part of Africa. The older children, after assembly, will be able to find Africa in an atlas, and will be able to see how far away from our country it is.

This boy's country, Ethiopia, is very hot, dry and sunny. The boy used to live in a small village, with his mother and father, his grandparents, and his brothers and sisters. He had friends and neighbours in the village as well. He knew everyone and everyone knew him. The people in the village were poor. They didn't have any money, but they didn't need any. They grew a few crops for food, and most of the villagers had a few cows, which gave them milk to drink and to make into cheese. When the cows were killed they provided the people with meat and leather. The boy's family didn't have many possessions, just a few pots and pans, and some mats to sleep on.

The boy's house was a hut, with just one room. All his large family slept there; they spent all day outside.

For the first six years of the boy's life, he was quite happy. His life was very different from yours, but he was used to his way of life.

And then, everything changed.

One year, the rain didn't come. It simply did not rain at all, for the whole of the year. The crops did not grow because there was no water. This stopped the cows giving milk, then many of them died, because they had no water. The boy and his family became hungry. No-one in the village had any food. The villagers walked to the nearest town and sold all their pots and pans and mats so that they could buy a little rice. Then they walked back home.

The following year, things became even worse. The rain still didn't come. No crops grew and the rest of the cows died. Even worse, people began to die because they were starving. Lots of people in the village died, especially the very old people, and the very young children. They seemed to become ill more easily than the other people. The boy's grandparents died, then his little sister died.

After that the boy's mother and father decided that they must not stay in the village any longer. If they stayed they knew they would die. They decided to walk back to the town and beg for food. By now they were all so weak that the journey was hard and tiring. When they reached the town they were turned away.

'There's no food here,' the people said, 'go to the camp over there.' The family looked and saw a big walled camp with hundreds of people inside. The people were sitting quietly, waiting their turn for food. Some helpers were sharing out food and water and medicines, but there was not enough to go round. The people who did not get any food, died. The boy and his family quietly walked into the camp, and waited in the long, long, queue to see if there would be any food for them.

I don't know if that boy was given some food, and stayed alive; or if there was no food for him, and he died. I do know that there are hundreds and hundreds of people like him in Africa, who do not have enough to eat, and hundreds more people who do not have anything to eat.

Many people are trying to help the starving people in countries like Africa. You will have heard of organisations like Oxfam, Christian Aid, Save the Children, and the Red Cross. All the people in those organisations are trying to help families like this boy's family.

Perhaps you might be able to think of a way in which you could help. You can certainly make sure you do not forget that there are many, many people in the world who do not have food to eat, or warm clothes to wear, or houses to live in, like you do.

Next time you have something to eat, remember the boy in the story, who was hungry.

Prayer

Thank you, Lord, for food to eat.
Thank you, Lord, for clothes to wear.
Thank you, Lord, for all your gifts.
Help us to help those who do not have these things.

Amen

Hymn
'Thank you, Lord, for this new day' **C&P**

*I displayed a simple poster, showing an African boy who was homeless and hungry. I found a single picture to have a greater impact on the children, than a collection of posters and photographs. Posters etc. are available from

several of the relief organisations mentioned in the assembly. I was forwarded a most useful informative pack from Oxfam, which formed the basis of a display, mounted after the assembly. This in turn led to a major fund raising activity in which children and parents joined. Oxfam also included knitting patterns for garments suitable for children in the Third World countries. These formed a secondary part of our appeal.

Harvest Festival

Week 6   Harvest

A children's assembly

Today, the children from five classes are going to take our Harvest Festival assembly. The children have been thinking about all the food and other useful things that we harvest from the land and sea. The children have brought some of their models and paintings for you to see. They have also started to make a harvest display table, here at the front of the hall, but this isn't yet finished. Perhaps they will finish it this morning.*

1st class

Child 1   We have been thinking about the harvest of the fields and have brought bread for the harvest table.

All sing   'When the corn is planted' **SSL**

Child 2   Where did you get the loaf of bread?

Child 3   I bought it from the supermarket. (picture)

Child 2   Where did the shop get the bread from?

Child 4   The baker sent it in a delivery van. (picture)

Child 2   Where did the baker get it from?

Child 5   The baker made the loaf out of flour and yeast and water. He mixed the dough, and kneaded the dough, and baked the loaves of bread. (picture)

Child 2   Where did he get the flour from?

Child 6   The miller made the flour by grinding corn. (picture)

Child 2   Where did the miller get the corn from?

Child 7   The farmer grew the corn in his fields. He planted the seeds, and the rain and sun made the corn grow and ripen. (picture)

All sing   'The farmer comes to scatter the seed' **SSL**

2nd class

Child 1   We have been thinking about the harvest of the hedgerows and have brought blackberries, rose hips, and crab apples for the harvest table.

All sing 'Look for signs that summer's done' **SSL**
Child 2   My mum makes me apple and blackberry pies. I like them with custard. (picture)
Child 3   At school we sometimes have red rose-hip syrup with rice pudding. (picture)
Child 4   My grandma makes pots of crab-apple jelly. (picture)
Child 5   My mum buys baskets of mushrooms from the shops. (picture)
Child 6   Hedgerow food is food for free. It gives us blackberry pies and jam for tea.
          But berries can be dangerous!
          Mushrooms can be poisonous!
          Don't let me pick food without an adult there with me. (pictures)
All sing 'Blackberries in the hedges' **MHB**

3rd class

Child 1   We have been thinking about the harvest of the sea. We have brought fish for the harvest table.
All sing 'When lamps are lighted' **SSL**
Child 1   My favourite food is fish and chips.
Child 2   Mine is sardines on toast.
Child 3   I like fish fingers and parsley sauce dips.
Child 4   I like hot fish cakes the most.
Child 5   Fish in a paper, fish on a plate
          Fish in a pie is the best.
Child 6   Fish from the sea makes the best sort of tea
          And breakfast and lunch and the rest.
All say   We thank the fishermen who go
          To sea, in boats trimmed neat;
          We thank them for the fish they bring
          To shore, for us to eat.
          (picture of trawler, nets and fish)

4th class
Child 1   We have been thinking about the harvest from under the ground. We have brought coal and oil for the havest table.
All sing The miners go down in the coal mine
          Dig in the ground, (picture)
          Dig in the ground,
          The miners go down in the coal mine;
          Bring up the coal to the top.

The oilmen go out to the oil field
Drill under the sea,
Drill under the sea, (picture)
The oilmen go out to the oil field
Bring up the oil to the top.
(to the tune 'The flowers that grow in the garden' **SSL**)

Child 2   We put coal on the fire to keep our houses warm. (picture)
Child 3   Coal is used in power stations to make electricity. (picture)
Child 4   Oil is used to make petrol, and that makes our cars go. (models)
All sing   There are treasures found under the ground
Deep underground,
Deep underground,
There is goal and gas and oil and metal
Deep down underneath the ground.
(to tune as above)

5th class
Child 1   We have been thinking about the harvest of the land, and have
brought fruits and vegetables for the harvest table.
All sing   'In my little garden' **A**
Child 2   I like red: red apples, red cherries, red strawberries, red raspber-
ries, red tomatoes. (pictures)
Child 3   I like orange: orange peaches, orange carrots, orange tangerines.
(pictures)
Child 4   I like yellow: yellow lemons, yellow grapefruits, yellow parsnips,
yellow swedes. (pictures)
Child 5   I like green: green grapes, green limes, green peas, green pears,
green gooseberries, green beans. (pictures)
Child 6   I like purple: purple plums, purple grapes, purple bilberries.
All sing   'See here are red apples' **C&S**

Prayer
Thank you, God, for the harvest.
Thank you for the harvest of the land, the harvest of the sea,
and the harvest from under the ground.
Thank you for all the good things we eat, for our clothes,
and our warm homes.
Help us to harvest our land well, and to share our harvest with others.

Amen

A harvest table was prepared prior to the assembly, with a colourful picture background of various foods etc. As the harvest festival proceeded, the display of actual produce grew, as each class added its contribution to the assembly.

This assembly 'plan' can be adapted to become as simple or complicated as required. The time can be reduced by eliminating one hymn per section. The brief dialogue could, if required, be elaborated to become a small play. Other sections to include other forms of harvest could be added. The possibilities are numerous.

These five harvest themes fitted our school's suburban setting. The themes could be altered and adapted to suit inner city or rural areas, to be meaningful for the children.

One third of the world is hungry   *Week 6   Harvest*

Yesterday, we had our Harvest Festival assembly, and we made a display of lots of different foods that we have to eat. We are very lucky, we have plenty to eat. Every day we have breakfast, and lunch, and tea, and supper, and I expect you have fruit or sweets, and drinks between your meals sometimes.

Every week I go to the shops. I suppose your parents do, too; perhaps you go with them to buy food for your family. I have brought my shopping for this week into assembly. I'll unpack my shopping bag, and add the things to our harvest table.*

Over here, at this side of the hall, opposite our harvest table, is another table. On this table is just one bowl of cooked rice.

I have chosen six children to help me today. They each have a plate. I will ask them to stand here, between the two tables.

I will give the first child a spoonful of rice. I will give nothing to the second child, and nothing to the third child. I will give a spoonful of rice to the fourth child, and nothing to the next two children.

Now, is that fair? No, it's not fair because two children have some rice, but four children have nothing.

I'll try to put it right. The four children who have nothing may go to the harvest table, and may choose as much as they like to put on their plates. Choose plenty.

Now, is that fair? No, of course it's not, because now, four children have lots of food, but these two children have only a little bit of rice. Four children could choose what they wanted, but these two children could not choose. Four children have full plates, but these two children have plates that are nearly empty.

The world is like these children. Some of us have lots to eat, but some people in the world do not have enough. Two out of every three people have plenty; one out of every three people has not enough. Two thirds of the world is full; one third of the world is hungry.

This week when we are thinking about the harvest and all the delicious things we have to eat, let's make sure we remember to think about all those people who are starving.

Prayer

Dear God,Thank you for the harvest,
> Thank you for our food;
> Help us to remember
> Those who have no food.
> Thank you for the harvest,
> Help us all to share;
> Help us all to share our world
> And make the portions fair.

Amen

Hymn
'Kum ba Yah' **C&P**

*The harvest display table used in the previous assembly was set at one side of the front of the hall, and to this was added the contents of the shopping bag. (This included items of appeal to the children which were not already in the display, eg. tins of soup and beans, sweets, biscuits, coffee, fruit juices, nuts, crisps etc.)

The table set at the other side of the hall, was deliberately left bare, except for the single bowl of cooked rice, to show a stark comparison between the two tables. I arranged the six children behind small tables which linked the two display tables.

The selfish giant
adapted from Oscar Wilde

Week 7   Unselfishness

Sometimes, when people live alone, they can become a little selfish, because there is no-one else in their house that they have to think about, or consider. When people live together in families, like you do at home, or like we all do at school, we cannot be completely selfish, because that way we would make life unpleasant for someone else. We have to learn to think of others, and to be unselfish, if we are all to live together happily.

There was once a giant who lived all alone in a large house with a very big, very beautiful garden. He had been away on holiday for quite some time, visiting another giant, and while he was away on holiday, the children used to go and play in his garden. It was a beautiful garden with colourful flowers, soft green grass and peach trees to climb; just the right sort of garden for children to play in.

One day the giant came home and was furious to find children in his garden. 'Out', he shouted. 'My own garden is my own garden! No-one may play in it, but me.' And he built a huge, high, stone wall round his garden to keep the children out. 'He's a selfish giant', everyone said.

During the winter, the children had to play in the stony lane outside the walls of the giant's garden. 'I wish we could play inside', they said. In the springtime the stony lane grew green with grass, the hedges became white with may blossom, and birds sang from the high branches; but everyone noticed the strangest thing in the giant's garden. There, inside the walls it was still winter, the trees were bare, the grass was covered with snow, the wind whistled round the house corners, and no birds sang.

'It's because he's so selfish', said the people. 'Spring won't visit his garden. His heart is cold, so his garden will stay cold, in winter's icy grip.'

The children wanted to see inside the giant's winter snowy-garden. They found a small hole in the wall, and climbed through. They gazed across the snow to the trees, then ran to them and climbed up into their bare branches. As soon as the garden saw that the children had come again it called to the spring to chase the winter away. The north wind vanished and the air became warm; the snow melted and spring flowers came pushing through the brown earth; the grass grew green; and best of all, each child-filled tree became covered in pink and white peach blossom, and sang with the song of the birds in its branches.

All, that is, except one. In the farthest corner of the garden, a tiny child could not reach up to climb into the tree. The tree bent its branches near to the ground, but still the child could not reach. Here, it was still winter. Here was still snow on the branches, and no blossom. The tiny child began to cry.

At that moment, the sound of the birds woke the giant. He sat up, rubbed his eyes, and looked out of his window at the spring and the children in his garden.

'It's beautiful', he said, and his old heart melted. 'Now I know why the spring did not come. I was selfish and mean. The children will share my garden.' Quietly he went outside. The children ran away when they saw him coming, but the tiny child with the tears in his eyes did not see the giant walking across the grass. Gently, the giant picked up the small child and lifted him into the tree. The winter left the tree, and it too became covered in beautiful blossom. The giant smiled. When the other chidlren saw the giant smile, they came out from their hiding places behind the wall.

'Please share my garden,' said the giant, 'I'm sorry I was selfish', and he took an axe and knocked the wall down.

When the people came home from market at the end of the day, they found the giant playing with the children in the most beautiful garden they had ever seen.

The story does not say whether the giant was sad or happy at the beginning or the end of the story. Since he smiled at the end of the story, and joined the children in their games, I think he was much happier than at the beginning when he was alone. People, like the giant are usually happiest when they are sharing things with their friends.

Prayer
Dear God, please help us not to be selfish.
Help us to think of other people and not just of ourselves.
Help us to share what we have with others.

Amen

Hymn
'Give me oil in my lamp' **C&P**

The hobgoblin
Week 7   Unselfishness

The story of the selfish giant, which we listened to in our last assembly, ended happily, I'm pleased to say. The giant, although he was very selfish at the beginning of the story, changed and soon learned to share his garden with the children. Today's story does not have such a happy ending! It is also about someone who was selfish, but he didn't learn until something dreadful happened.

It all started when a farmer in Ireland had nearly finished ploughing his six acre field. The day was hot, the work was hard, and the farmer stopped to mop his brow. As he gazed across the last piece of earth towards the bramble-hedge, he noticed a movement, a twitch of green, a flash of blue, and a tiny hand waving. 'Help', called a voice from the thorns. The farmer walked towards the hedge and saw a small hobgoblin caught by his blue jacket in the thorns. Now hobgoblins are not uncommon in that part of Ireland, so the farmer was not unduly surprised.

'Set me free please', said the hobgoblin. 'I'll repay you well if you do.'

Now this farmer was not one to miss a bargain. 'What will you give me if I set you free?' he said.

'I have magic powers,' answered the hobgoblin, 'I'll give you my help whenever you need it. Just set me free.'

'I know you hoodwinking hobgoblins', said the farmer. 'If I set you free I'll never see you again. I'll get no help from you when I need it.' And the farmer carefully disentangled the hobgoblin from the thorns, but instead of setting him free, he stuffed the hobgoblin into his pocket, leaving just his head sticking out. Then the farmer ran home. He locked the hobgoblin in the kitchen, went into his shed, and made a wooden cage, just the right size for the hobgoblin. Then back he went to the kitchen, set the cage on the window sill, and put the hobgoblin inside.

'There', said the farmer. 'You can live in this cage in my kitchen. If ever I need any help I'll be able to ask you. After all, I did set you free from the thorns.'

'But you haven't set me free', wailed the hobgoblin. 'This is as bad as being caught in a bramble hedge. I should be free, not caged, please let me out.' But the farmer would not let the hobgoblin out of the cage. He fed him, and let him look out on the world from the kitchen window sill, but he would not set the hobgoblin free.

Soon word went round the village that the farmer had a magic hobgoblin in a cage; a hobgoblin that could help anyone who needed help. Before the end of the day there was a queue of people at the door, all wanting the farmer to ask the hobgoblin for help.

'I've lost my sheepdog', said the shepherd. 'Will you please ask your hobgoblin to help me find him?'

'No, he can't help you, he's my hobgoblin', said the farmer.

'My son is very ill', said a neighbouring farmer. 'Can your hobgoblin do anything to help?'

'No, he can't help you, he's my hobgoblin', said the farmer.

'I'm having great difficulty harvesting my corn', said yet another farmer. 'I need more help, will you lend me your hobgoblin?'

'No, he can't help you, he's my hobgoblin', said the farmer.

'I desperately need some help', said the apple farmer. 'There are maggots in all my apples, can your hobgoblin help?'

'No', said the farmer, 'he's my hobgoblin.'

The farmer was not going to allow the hobgoblin to help anyone else but himself. He sent all the rest of the people in the queue home.

That night the farmer awoke with a feeling that something was wrong. He looked out of his bedroom window, and there across the farmyard he could see flames and smoke. His hay barn was on fire. All his valuable hay was being destroyed.

'The hobgoblin will be able to help', he thought. 'With his magical powers he will be able to put everything right.' The famer pulled on his clothes and ran downstairs to the kitchen. He went to the cage on the windowsill. The hobgoblin was gone. He had vanished, disappeared; escaped. The farmer rushed outside and threw buckets of water from the yard pump onto the barn. He managed to stop the fire spreading further, but his barn and all his hay was burned to the ground.

'What a waste. Oh what a waste', moaned the farmer. 'My selfishness has caused this. If I hadn't tried to keep the hobgoblin all to myself, he would have kept his word and would have helped me. I have stopped him helping me, and stopped him helping all my friends and neighbours as well. But I have learned my lesson. I will never be selfish and greedy again.'

And the farmer tried very hard to keep his word.

I hope that if you find a trapped hobgoblin, you will set it free! I also hope that if you have some good luck you will want to share it with your family and friends.

Prayer

    Dear God, if we find something that is not ours to keep,
        help us to return it to where it belongs.
    Teach us not to be selfish when others need help.
    Help us to help others, when we can.

Amen

Hymn
'When I needed a neighbour' **C&P**

The widow's gift
adapted from Buddhist scriptures

    Week 7   Unselfishness

There is a story that Buddhists tell about an old lady who was very unselfish. The Buddha told a gathering of people that she was so unselfish she was an example to everyone, and they each could learn from her, even though she was the poorest of them all.

One day the Buddha arrived in a town and said 'I am collecting presents to give to the poor. If you have something you could give away, to help the poor and needy, please bring it to me today. I will sit here under this tree and wait for your gifts.'

The Buddha, in his saffron-yellow robes, settled himself down under the shade of the Banyan tree at the edge of the town, and waited. The people scurried away to their homes to search for things to bring to the Buddha, to give to the poor and needy.

Soon a long procession of people was wending its way through the narrow streets of the town, towards the seated Buddha. Every person in the queue was carrying something from his home to give away to the Buddha. There were parcels and packages of all shapes and sizes. There were baskets of gifts and presents wrapped in long rolls of cloth. Even the King and Queen were there; they carried small parcels, but their servants were laden with gifts to give to the Buddha.

The Buddha, sitting under the shade of the Banyan tree, looked at the people with their gifts and said 'How kind you are. How good it is that you all give so much to help the poor people of our country. Please put your gifts here next to me, under the shade of this tree.'

The King was the first to step forward. 'I have brought a casket of fine jewels', he said, handing the seated Buddha a jewel-encrusted box. 'My servants have brought furniture made of the finest gold and silver', he added, importantly.

'Thank you', said the Buddha from his place beneath the tree. 'Please put the things here at my side', and he pointed to the place he meant.

The King stood aside and smiled at the waiting queue of people, as if to say 'Look what fine things I have brought'.

Then the Queen stepped forward. 'I have brought beautiful cloth for the poor people to wear', she said. 'Look, it has gold and silver threads in it. All my servants are carrying more cloth. I have brought you the best cloth from the palace', and she stood aside as if to say 'Haven't I brought wonderful gifts?'

'Thank you', said the Buddha from his place beneath the tree. 'Please put the things here at my side', and he pointed to the place.

Then, one by one, the rest of the people in the queue stepped forward and gave the Buddha their gifts. There were many precious things given, for there were many rich people living in the town. Each time the Buddha received a gift he said 'Thank you', from his place beneath the tree.

At the end of the day, the pile of gifts was as high as the tree itself, and everyone had given their present. Everyone, that is, except one very old lady. She shuffled towards the Buddha, her torn old clothes flapping, and held out a pomegranate.

'Please take this', she whispered. 'I was just going to eat this pomegranate when I heard you were collecting for the poor. I'd like you to have it instead. It's nothing much, but I haven't anything else to give.'

She gave the Buddha the pomegranate and turned to go away but the Buddha stood up, took hold of her hands and said 'Stay. Sit by me. I want to thank you. Lots of people have given lots of gifts today, but you have given more than anyone. Thank you.'

The King and Queen and all the people who were watching were angry with the Buddha when they heard this. 'What are you saying', they shouted, 'we have given more than just a silly pomegranate!'

'Listen', said the Buddha. 'You have given a small share of what you own. This woman has given everything she owns, she has nothing else left. She has given more than any of you because she has given everything she has.'

Sometimes, nowadays, we are asked to give money to help people. Sometimes organisations have flag days or collections so that people can help by giving. It doesn't matter how much money people put in. What matters is that people give what they can afford. When we had our harvest festival, we had an appeal to help the African people. Lots of you gave different amounts of money, but that didn't matter. The important thing was that lots of people helped, and all the money, even the small amounts, all added up to help. We all tried to be unselfish and we all tried to help.

Prayer

Teach us, Lord, not to be selfish.
Teach us to think of others not just ourselves.
Teach us, like the old woman in the story,
    to give what we can, to help.

Amen

Hymn
'The family of man' **C&P**

Anna's memory   *Week 8   Remembering*

Sometimes it is quite hard remembering to do things. I don't have a very good memory, and often I have to write things down, or find other ways of making sure I remember things. Usually those memory joggers work, and as you know, I don't often forget things, but that's because I work hard at making sure I remember.

Today's story is about a girl called Anna. She was about the same age as some of you, but unlike most of you, she had an *awful* memory. She forgot *everything*. Her teacher used to say, 'It's no use asking Anna to do that, she'll forget.' Her mother used to say, 'It's no good asking Anna to help, she'll forget what to do.' Her friends used to say, 'It's no good asking Anna to come, she'll forget'.

Anna forgot everything, but the sad part about it all was that she didn't really have a bad memory at all; she just didn't bother to think, and she never thought about other people's feelings.

One day it was Anna's mum's birthday. Anna's mum had been looking forward to her birthday all week. Birthdays were special, even if you were grown up, and usually Anna's dad, grandma and little brother did something nice to make her mum's birthday special. Last year everyone in the family had planted some new rose trees in the garden, and had taken Anna's mum out for a special birthday tea. But this year Anna's grandma was poorly, her dad was very busy at work, and Anna had forgotten about her mum's birthday.

Anna got up, had her breakfast, grabbed her schoolbag, and rushed out to school, shouting goodbye to her mum. She didn't even remember to say Happy Birthday. Her mum looked sad, but she didn't say anything. It was just as though Anna didn't care.

When Anna got to school, she went into her classroom and got out her things. She hadn't put away her reading book the day before, and now she couldn't remember where it was. Then she couldn't find her pencil case, she'd forgotten whether it was at home or at school, and she thought she'd lost it. By playtime her teacher was thoroughly cross with her, because she wasn't even trying to remember anything – it was just as though she didn't care.

At playtime Anna went to find Sarah and John and started to play a game with them, but halfway through she remembered that she'd told two of her other friends that she would play with them at playtime. So Anna left Sarah and John and went across the playground to the others, but when she got there the game was already started and they didn't want Anna to join in. They said it was her fault for not remembering to come at the beginning of playtime. She went back to play with John and Sarah, but now they didn't want her to play either.

'I don't care', Anna said to herself, but she did care really.

At in–time Anna's teacher said, 'Anna, why didn't you take the box of straws to class 2? You promised you would.'

'I forgot', said Anna.

'You are selfish and thoughtless', said her teacher. 'You didn't forget – you just didn't think. There's nothing the matter with your memory; you just don't care enough to remember. It's time you learned to be responsible and to care for the people around you, not just yourself.'

Anna sat at her table and tried hard not to cry. She did care really. Deep down inside her, she cared very much about her friends, her mum and the family, her teacher and school. Perhaps though she hadn't shown people that she cared. Perhaps if she stopped to think she could find a way of showing she cared.

That afternoon Anna tried harder. She remembered it was her mum's birthday, and made her a card. At playtime, before she did anything else, she stopped to think. She remembered about the straws, and took them to class 2. Then she went out to play. She looked around and saw Helen standing by herself, so Anna went to play with Helen. By the end of the day she discovered that by stopping to think she could remember more, and she could show people she cared by remembering to do things.

We can show people we care, by remembering to do things for them, and by remembering to be thoughtful and kind.

Prayer
Dear God, help us to show the people we care about, that we do care, by remembering to do things, and by remembering to be thoughtful and considerate. Help us to be responsible by remembering to do things at the right time.

Amen

Hymn
'Think, think on these things' **SSL**

Androcles and the lion
Week 8   Remembering

Stories tell us that of all the animals, elephants are supposed to have the longest memóries. 'An elephant never forgets', people say. I know a story of another animal that once had a very good memory: its good memory saved the life of a man called Androcles.

Androcles was a Christian and he lived a long, long time ago, in the days when Christians could be put to death for their beliefs.

One day Androcles was travelling through the mountains on a lonely pathway. He was nervous about the journey he had to make, as the mountains in those days were dangerous places, where wild animals roamed, and where bands of robbers often laid in wait for travellers.

Suddenly, Androcles' worst fears became real, as he heard the long, loud roar of a lion. Androcles stood quite still on the path as the lion came out from behind the bushes. The lion roared again and then sank down on the ground, as though it were in pain. Androcles didn't know what to do; the lion was in his way, so he couldn't go on; he was afraid to turn and run away in case the lion should run and pounce on him, so he couldn't go back. Androcles stayed perfectly still, afraid to move, for what seemed like a very long time. The lion roared again, stretched out its front paw . . . and groaned.

It was then Androcles saw that the lion's front paw was red and swollen. The lion was in dreadful pain.

Androcles quietly and gently walked forward along the path until he was close enough to touch the lion. The lion lay quite still and did not snarl or growl at Androcles. Gently Androcles examined the lion's paw. He found a long, sharp thorn sticking into the pad of the paw. Carefully he pulled out the thorn. Then he soaked a piece of cloth in the water of a nearby stream, and washed and cleaned the lion's paw. All the time that Androcles was doing this, the lion lay quite still. When Androcles had finished cleaning the paw, the lion made a sound like a big cat purring, stood up, and moved off into the bushes again.

Androcles went on his way through the mountains.

During the next few months soldiers were ordered to capture and kill all men who were followers of Jesus. One day Androcles was captured.

'Are you a Christian?' asked the soldier.

'Yes, I am', answered Androcles.

'Say you are not a Christian and you can live', said the soldier. 'If you say you are a Christian, I shall have to kill you.'

'I cannot tell a lie', said Androcles.

'Then you will die', said the soldier.

So Androcles was taken prisoner and put in jail. The next day he was to be thrown into a den of lions, for that was the way the Christians were killed in those days.

In the morning Androcles was taken to the arena where a fierce, hungry lion was waiting. All around the arena were crowds of people, waiting and watching to see the Christian killed and eaten by the lion.

Androcles was pushed into the arena, and the gate clanged shut behind him. The crowd roared and shouted as they waited for the kill. The lion slowly walked towards Androcles, who closed his eyes and fell to his knees.

'Please let me be killed quickly', he prayed, 'so that I don't feel too much pain.' Androcles held his breath. He could feel the warmth of the lion's body near him. He could feel the warm breath of the lion on his face. He felt the soft touch of the lion's nose against his skin. Then he felt the lion gently licking his hand. He noticed how silent the crowd had become. Androcles opened his eyes in astonishment. Why had he not been killed? The lion sat on the ground and raised one of its front paws for Androcles to see. The paw had a tiny scar on its pad.

Androcles understood. This was his lion. This was the lion whose paw he had cleaned and bathed. This was the lion he had helped all those months before, and now the lion was helping Androcles. Androcles bent down to put his arms around the lion's neck.

The crowd gasped in amazement.

'This man must be set free', they said.
'This man, that a lion will not eat, must be freed.'
And so Androcles, and the lion, were both set free.

Androcles was lucky that the lion remembered him, and the lion not only remembered, but knew that one good turn deserves another.

We should try to remember when people are kind to us, and try to repay their kindness in some way. That way, kindness and caring grow. A school where people are kind and caring is usually a happy school Let's make sure our school is like that.

Prayer

Dear God, please help us to show someone a kindness every day.
Help us to be thoughtful and considerate towards others, all the time.

Amen

Hymn
'When I needed a neighbour' **C&P**

Remembrance Day   *Week 8   Remembering*

This week in our assemblies, we have been thinking about remembering. I expect most of you know that Sunday is called Remembrance Sunday, when we think about all the soldiers who have died or been wounded, fighting for our country, since the First World War. You all know that we have been helping to sell poppies. You know that the money from the poppies will go towards helping disabled soldiers and their families; but perhaps you don't know why poppies were chosen as the symbol of the money raising fund.

For a long time it seemed that there would be trouble between the countries, and then on one dreadful day in 1914 an Austrian Archduke was shot by a man from another country called Serbia. The countries argued, the governments of other countries joined in, and soon it seemed that the whole world was at war. It was a terrible war. There were guns and tanks, injuries and deaths. People thought the war would end in the winter, but it went on through the winter, into the next summer and on and on, summer and winter for four years.

A commander called Earl Haig was sent from England to a place called Flanders in Europe, where the fighting was particularly bad. The soldiers were living in dug out trenches in the fields. The trenches were just long holes in the ground. When it rained, huge puddles formed in the bottom of the trenches and the sides turned to oozing mud. In those trenches the men had to eat, sleep, and fight, if the enemies came near. The soldiers became wet, cold, hungry, ill and unhappy, but they couldn't run away, they had to stay. Earl Haig went into the trenches with the soldiers. Day and night they stayed in the trenches, only coming out to fight. Day and night the skies were red with fires and flames and explosions. Many men were killed or injured. There was no safe place for the injured men to go. The few doctors managed to look after the soldiers as best they could. Earl Haig was afraid, but like the soldiers, he couldn't run away.

While the fighting was going on, the leaders of all the countries had met together to talk about the war.

'It's gone on too long', they said.

'Too many soldiers have been killed', they said.

'It's time the war was stopped', they said.

And so, all the leaders of the countries signed an agreement to say the fighting would stop. Messengers were sent to the soldiers on the battle fields. The messengers struggled through the fighting, and delivered the news. The agreement had been signed, the fighting must stop.

At 11 o'clock on the 11th day of November (the 11th month), four years after the war had started, the fighting stopped. Peace was declared.

The men began to crawl out of the trenches. They were tired, dirty, ill and wounded. Slowly they began to go home.

Earl Haig climbed out of his trench. He looked around him and saw weary men coming through the mud. He saw other soldiers lying dead or injured. Then he looked beyond the mud to where the grass was growing, and there he could see hundreds and hundreds of bright red poppies, nodding and waving in the breeze. Earl Haig looked back at the soldiers.

'We will remember them', he said. 'We will remember every soldier who has fought to save our country.'

And Earl Haig, too, went home.

After that, a group of people began to make artificial poppies to sell, to raise money to help the wounded soldiers and their families.

Every year, on November 11th, we too, remember all the soldiers who fought so bravely. We remember them by wearing a poppy for 'Poppy Day'. If you watch television on Sunday, in the morning, you will see a special service in London, where the Royal Family, and the leaders of our country remember the soldiers by putting poppy wreaths round the base of the Cenotaph.

Prayer

At 11 o'clock, on the 11th day of November, the 11th month, in 1918, all the fighting stopped between the countries which were at war, because a peace agreement had been signed. The fighting was over.

Today we remember all the people who were killed or injured in war. We pray that our world leaders will work hard to let our countries be at peace with each other.

Amen

Hymn

'Peace, perfect peace' **C&P**

Alfred – the great king

Week 9   Reading

A long time ago, most people did not have the chance to learn to read and write, as you do at school. There were hardly any books; there were no colourful story books like the ones you have, the few books that were available, were only for rich people, and were written and drawn by hand. There were no printing machines to make books as we know them. Some people did not think it was important to learn to read and write.

Just over a thousand years ago there were two princes called Ethelred and Alfred. Their father was the King of Wessex. Their mother, the Queen, was anxious that both brothers should learn to read and write and she employed a wise man to teach them both. This man worked hard to teach both boys to read the Bible, but they both found it hard work.

Ethelred said, 'Why do I have to bother with this? Reading is no good. I shall be king one day and I will need to be able to fight and lead my people, not sit at home and read the Bible. I don't want to learn any more.'

But Alfred said, 'I, too, may be king one day. I will need to lead my people, but I want to be a wise leader. I think learning to read will help me to be wise.' So Alfred tried hard with his work, and soon he was able to read and write well.

The day came when Ethelred was made King of all Wessex. It was a difficult time, as the kingdom was under attack from the Vikings. They came across the sea in great ships, landed on England's shores, burnt down villages, killed anyone who got in their way and attacked and beat Ethelred's armies. Ethelred was not a wise man, and seemed always to organise his armies too late. They were never ready in time for battle and people started to call their King Ethelred the Unready. One day, he was so unready he was killed!

Now was the time for Alfred to become king; but the people were now so afraid of the Vikings, who had beaten their armies and who were ruling their kingdom, that they all ran away to hide in the marshes. Poor Alfred had no kingdom over which to be king. But Alfred was a wise man, and he thought of a plan. He too went to the marshes with his people. He gathered a group of people together and taught them to read and write. Then he sent out those people to teach others to do the same. Meanwhile he collected brave, strong men for his army. He didn't take all the men from every family, he was wise enough to take some and leave some to defend the women and children. Slowly the army was gathered . . . slowly the plan was formed . . . slowly the people learned to read and write.

At last the day came when Alfred's new army was ready to do battle and to overthrow Guthrum the king of the Vikings. Silently, messengers travelled to each homestead in the marshes, silent messages, written down on pieces of paper were handed from one to another. The whole army was ready to attack, and because of the silent, written messages, the enemy knew nothing about it, until it happened. The battle was instant and fierce. Guthrum and the Vikings were defeated, Alfred was victorious. Guthrum retreated to a neighbouring kingdom, and Alfred, in his wisdom wrote down a peace treaty, which when each king had signed, promised that they would live without fear from the other, in their neighbouring kingdoms.

Alfred was now truly King of Wessex, the people looked up to him and called him Alfred the Great. Alfred and Guthrum's peace treaty ended the worst Viking fighting. Alfred's sons and grandsons later were able to drive the Vikings out of England completely, but that's another story.

Alfred was truly a great king, and he proved that it wasn't enough just to be able to fight. He proved that reading and writing helped him and his people to win battles. Later, Alfred set up schools, where many more people, especially children, were taught to read and write.

Prayer
>Thank you, God, for our schools and teachers.
>Thank you for the chances we have to learn to read and write.
>Help us to make the most of those opportunities,
>>and to do our best in everything we do.
>>>>>>>>>>*Amen*

Hymn
'The ink is black' **C&P**

The finding-out argument

One of the things I like to do most of all at the end of the day, when I've finished doing all my work for school and at home, is to read. I like to sit by the fire, or if it is warm in summer I like to sit in the garden. I like to read books, newspapers and magazines. I go to the library near my house, and I borrow books to read. Sometimes, I choose a book to give me information; this week I borrowed a book about photography. Sometimes I choose a book to tell me about other countries and other people. Sometimes I just choose a good story, a book that I will simply enjoy reading, because I like reading. I like to buy books as well as borrowing them from the library. When I buy a book, I know that book belongs to me, and I know I can look at it whenever I want to. I have quite a lot of books at home, and every so often I have to buy a new bookcase to put them all in. I think I shall soon need a bigger house to put all the bookcases in!

One day two children were playing together in a garden, and they were talking about books. 'I've got lots of books at home', said Leroy.
 'I bet I've got more books than you have', boasted Therèsa. ' I've got so many books at home, I can find out everything about anything.' As soon as she had said that, Therèsa was sorry, because although she did have many books at home, she knew she certainly didn't have books about everything.
 'That's stupid', answered Leroy. 'You can't find out everything from books. Anyway you haven't got all that many books in your house.'
 'You can find out anything from books', argued Therèsa.
 'Well, prove it', Leroy challenged. 'Find out why bread has holes in it!'
 Therèsa went home and hunted amongst her mum's cookery books. She found a page on baking bread, and she found that yeast is put into the bread mixture, that yeast is a kind of fungus, and that it gives off a gas whilst it is growing in the bread. The gas bubbles up through the dough and makes the holes.
 She went back to Leroy and gave him the information, and she showed him the book she had taken the information from.
 'See', she said, 'I was right. You can find out anything you want to know from books.'
 'Rubbish', he said. 'That question was just too easy. I bet you haven't got a book about boomerangs. Find out about them', and Leroy walked off.
 Therèsa was determined not to be beaten by him. First of all she found a dictionary to see what a boomerang was. She thought she knew but she wasn't sure. 'An Australian curved, hardwood weapon', she read. She went to look for the encyclopaedia her aunt had given her last Christmas. She

looked up B, then B O O: Books, Boom, Boots, – Boomerang wasn't there! Now she was stuck. She didn't want to admit to Leroy that she couldn't find the information; not after all she had said.

'I know', she thought. 'There is a big set of encyclopaedias in the school library. Boomerang is bound to be in there.'

The next day at school Therèsa asked if she could go into the school library at playtime. She took some paper and a pencil, and at playtime she set to work. Fifteen minutes later she had a whole page written down about boomerangs, and Australia, and the way of life of the Australian people.

'There, that'll show Leroy', she said to herself.

At lunchtime she gave her paper to Leroy.

'You see, I was right', she boasted. 'Anything can be found in books.'

All right', said Leroy, 'I agree. But you only half win. Anything can be found in books, but you can't find every piece of information in the books in your home.'

'All right', said Therèsa. 'You win as well.' And they shook hands on it, to end the argument.

Leroy and Therèsa both knew that just about any piece of information can be found in a book. The secret is knowing where to look. Dictionaries and encyclopaedias are good places to start looking.

When I was 12, I was given a set of encyclopaedias as a present. At the time I didn't think it was a very exciting present. But it was one of the most useful presents I've ever been given. Even now, although the books are quite old-fashioned, I still often look up information in them.

Prayer
Thank you, God, for all our books.
Thank you for all the information we can find in books.
Thank you for the people who gather that information together.

Amen

Hymn
'When a Knight won his spurs' **C&P**

The secret school   *Week 9   Reading*

I have a friend who is a teacher and who helps people to learn to read and write. Well, there is nothing unusual about that, you might say; all our teachers here at school help people to read and write. This particular teacher works at a kind of secret school, and all her pupils are not children, but grown-ups who go to her special school in the evenings. Sometimes the teacher goes to their houses to help them to learn to read and write.

One September, at the beginning of a new school year, the teacher had just three people in her class, two men and a lady. All three had come to the secret school because they were all ashamed of not being able to read and write. They were so ashamed that they didn't want anyone else to know that they couldn't read or write. They had all been to school when they were children; but Margaret Evans had been ill for a long time, and had missed a lot of school; Tom Harrison had been very lazy as a child and had simply not tried hard enough, and Henry Thompson had a father who was a farmer and who was always wanting his son to help on the farm instead of going to school, so Henry too had missed a great deal of school time. Now, all three of them wanted very much to be able to read and write like everyone else. You see, they found it very difficult not being able to read.

All three of them had found ways of getting round the problem, when they were with other people.

Tom Harrison kept a pair of broken glasses in his top pocket. If anyone asked him to read something he would say, 'Sorry, I can't see to read that, my glasses are broken.' And he would pull the broken glasses out of his pocket for everyone to see. Of course, Tom didn't need glasses at all, he just kept them as an excuse, so that he wouldn't have to admit that he couldn't read.

Henry Thompson still worked on his father's farm, and he wasn't often asked to read anything. One day he became very worried because he had to go into town to sign some very important papers. Just before he set off to town, he put bandages on both his hands. When he arrived at the office where he had to sign the papers, he told the people, 'You'll have to read the papers to me, I've hurt my hands in an accident and I can't hold the papers or a pen. You'll have to sign my name for me.' In the end a man very gently helped him to hold a pen and put a cross where his signature should go. Henry told them his hands were so painful, he couldn't manage more than that. The people all felt very sorry for him, but of course there was nothing wrong with his hands, he was too ashamed to admit that he couldn't read or write, so he'd made up that elaborate excuse.

Margaret Evans had a little girl of her own now, Elizabeth, who was six. So far Margaret had managed to keep it a secret from everyone, even Mr Evans, that she couldn't read very well. She could read a little, just easy words like cat, tree and house, and she could write her name, but nothing else. If she was in the doctor's waiting room, or on a bus, she would open a newspaper, or a magazine and pretend to read, so that everyone would think she could. But now, she had a problem because Elizabeth could read better than she could. Elizabeth used to bring books home from school and ask her mum to read them to her, and of course Margaret Evans couldn't do that. She felt ashamed because she couldn't read; just as ashamed as Tom Harrison and Henry Thompson.

The three grown-ups had decided, quite separately, to do something about their reading. The three went to the secret school. They had to be very brave and tell their families, but they didn't have to tell anyone else. They all three worked very hard, week after week after week, sometimes at the school and sometimes in their own homes. Slowly, each of them learned how to read a little, and how to write a little. They kept on practising in order to become better at reading and writing.

We are all lucky here at school. We all have the chance of learning to read. Let's make sure we work hard and make the most of that chance, and then we won't have to go to a secret school when we grow up.

Prayer (read by an older child in school)
> Dear God, thank you for our school.
> Help us to work hard and do our best,
>> so that we will be able to read and write well.
> Thank you for our teachers and parents who help us,
>> and for the books which help us, too.
>
> *Amen*

Hymn
'Thank you Lord for this new day' **C&P**

Anne Frank   *Week 10   Writing*

Last weekend I went shopping. I needed to buy some things for Christmas, but I also wanted to buy something for myself, something I always buy for myself every year. Here it is. Yes, it is a diary. This is the diary that I shall keep on my desk, and in which I shall write down all the things I have to remember to do at school. There are lots of different kinds of diaries.* Sometimes you write in a diary things which are going to happen, things you have to remember. Sometimes you write in a diary things which have happened, things you have enjoyed or disliked or how you have felt about things. Those are often the best diaries to write, because the diary becomes like a friend, that you tell all your secrets to. Those are often the most interesting diaries to read as well.

There was once a girl called Anne, who kept a diary. She was given the diary on her thirteenth birthday, and she promised herself that every day she would write down all the things she had done, and even thought about during the day. She would tell the diary everything. Anne was just an ordinary person, just like you but a little older, but some very extraordinary things happened to her. You see, Anne and her family were Jewish, and they were living in Holland, just before the beginning of the Second World War. At that time, soldiers were being sent to cities and towns to find Jewish people. When they were found they were sent to prison camps, and there they lived in dreadful conditions: that is if they lived at all. Usually they were starved or gassed or shot.

Anne's father, Mr Frank, knew that he had to do something to save his family. They couldn't leave Holland to go to another country, because the soldiers were at all the ports and borders, looking out for Jews trying to leave the country. Mr Frank knew that there were some secret rooms at the top of the office building where he worked. He decided that the safest thing would be for his family to hide there in those rooms. The family gathered together their most important possessions and they went to the office buildings. The rooms were up a narrow staircase; the door to the staircase was hidden by a big bookcase. Mr and Mrs Frank, Anne, and her older sister Margot crept behind the bookcase and up the stairs to the secret room. Friends, who knew of the secret, pushed the bookcase back over the door.

Every week their friends came to the secret door behind the bookcase and brought food and books. Every day Anne wrote in her diary about her life in the secret room. After a few weeks four more Jews joined the Franks in their hiding place. It must have been very hard for those eight people, living in a small secret place, never being able to go outside. It must have been especially hard for Anne, who was the youngest. She couldn't go out and play, or meet her friends. She couldn't go to school or take part in sports. She could only stay, quietly so that no-one would hear, in the secret rooms, playing games, or reading, or writing her diary. Anne and her family lived in the secret rooms for more than two years, and then the one thing they feared more than anything else, happened. The German soldiers found their secret hiding place. The soldiers captured all eight people and sent them to prison camps in Germany. During the next few years, seven of the eight died. Only Anne's father lived, and came home at the end of the war. Anne, her sister and mother, and the other four Jews who had shared the secret rooms, all died.

When Anne's father came home, he went again to the secret rooms, just to look at them. There, untouched by the German soldiers, were Anne's diaries. Her father read them, and decided that other people should read them as well, and so the diaries were made into books that everyone could read. They tell us of a brave girl who was cheerful and sensible, even though she was a prisoner in a secret hiding place.

It is good that Anne bothered to write her diary. Without it, we would never have known about the brave family, and how they coped for all that time.

Perhaps you could begin to keep a diary, and write down all the things that you do each day.

Prayer
Thank you, God, for the brave example of Anne Frank.
Thank you for the ability to think and write things down.
Help us to put those abilities to good use.

Amen

Hymn
'Give me oil in my lamp' **C&P**

*I made a small display of different types of diaries, to show the children, eg appointment, desk, pocket, page-a-day, week-a-spread, note-line calendar, blank note book. I also showed the children the school appointment diary, and the school log book.

The handwriting books   Week 10   Writing

In our last assembly, we heard the story of Anne Frank. It was a good thing that Anne took the trouble to write in her diary, or we would never have known about her life in the secret rooms. It was a good thing too that the writers of these books bothered to write down their stories, or we wouldn't have the Bible, or Aesop's fables, or Hans Andersen's Fairy Tales, or Roald Dahl's stories.*

Sometimes children say, 'Well, it's all right for those people, but I can't write very well yet, so I can't write stories.' Small children sometimes say that because they are just learning how to write. Older children sometimes say that because they are learning how to do joined up writing, and they may not yet be very good at it. But everyone has to start somewhere.

There was once a little girl whose birthday was at Easter-time. She started school on her fifth birthday, straight after the Easter holiday. She joined a class of children, many of whom had started school the September before. The little girl felt quite unhappy at first, because it seemed to her that all those other boys and girls could do such a lot, and it seemed that she could do so little; but most of those other children had been learning how to read and write and do sums for several months, and she had only just begun to learn, because she had only just started school. Some of the children could even write stories on their own, whilst she was still struggling to write her name without any mistakes.

Every day she tried her best, and every day she practised hard: and slowly, very slowly, her writing became a little better. I have brought her first and second writing books to show you.† You can see how hard she found it to write, at first; but in the second book, you can see that she is getting better.

The little girl tried hard with all her work, and she tried especially hard with her writing.

That little girl is now grown-up. She can write quite well now, in fact she is quite good at writing. She wrote down the words of our hymn this morning. You might recognise the handwriting?

Yes, you're right, it's my handwriting, and those books are my first school writing books, which my mum has kept all these years. So you see everyone has to start at the beginning; even all your teachers had to start at the beginning once upon a time. I found writing hard at first, but I kept on trying and practising, until, gradually, it became better.

If you all do your best, and try your hardest with your writing, yours will also become better.

Prayer

Let us think about trying our best *every* time we write something down.
Let us remember that practice makes perfect,
    and if we keep on trying our handwriting will get better.
Thank you, God, for pencils and crayons
    and all the things we write with.
Thank you, God, for paper and books to write on.
Thank you, God, for our brains and eyes, hands and fingers
    that we use each time we write.

Amen

Hymn

'Praise the Lord in everything' **C&P**

*I provided a simple display of well-known books, and books by well-known authors, to illustrate this point.   *†I am lucky enough to possess my first school work books. If yours are not available perhaps a member of staff has theirs, and an example of their adult writing (printing) can be shown to the children. Failing that, it would be possible to take 'poetic licence' with the idea, choose an example of the reception class' writing and an example of a top class child's writing, and make the necessary adaptation to the story.*

Louis Braille   *Week 10   Writing*

Just imagine what it would be like trying to write, if you couldn't see. Blind people sometimes need to write things down: they may want to write a letter to a friend who can see, or they may want to write a message for the plumber or the electrician coming to do repairs at their house. Perhaps you have sometimes tried to write with your eyes closed. The writing isn't easy to do; it is very hard to keep in straight lines, you can't look back to see what you've written, you just have to remember what you have put. It must be just as difficult for blind people. To help them to write they have a small wooden frame, about the size of a piece of writing paper, and stretched across the frame are lines of thin elastic. The blind person can then write his or her letter, feeling where the lines are. They still have to remember what they have already written down though, they can't look back to see what they have put; so the frame helps, but it is not ideal.

Blind people have another way of writing, a way that means they can also read the writing back to themselves, or read someone else's writing. They do not see the writing, they feel it with their fingers. This way of writing for blind people all started a long time ago in France. A little three-year-old boy was playing with his father's leather tools. He picked up a sharp knife and a piece of leather, as he had seen his father do, and he began to cut into the leather with the knife. The knife slipped and instead of cutting into the leather, it cut into the boy's eye. He screamed out in pain, and his mother and father came rushing to see what was the matter. They took the boy straightaway to the doctor's house, but the doctor could do nothing to save the boy's sight. The damaged eye became infected with a disease, which then spread to his other eye. In a short time the boy was blind. His name was Louis Braille.

When Louis was ten, he won a place at a school for blind children in Paris. His parents were very pleased, because although Paris was a long way off and Louis would have to live at the school, they knew that he was clever, and that with the help of the teachers he would do well. Louis worked hard and showed his teachers that he was one of the cleverest boys at the school. He learned to read by feeling letters which had been stamped onto paper to make the letter-shapes raised. The method was not very good, and Louis thought there must be a better way of helping blind people to read.

A few years later, a new method of teaching blind people to read and write, was invented. This method used raised dots instead of raised letters, and was a little easier to use, but Louis still didn't think it was very good. He decided there was only one thing to do: to invent a new method himself. After all, he was blind, so he knew what blind people wanted and needed.

Every evening after his day at school was finished, Louis sat in his room and did experiment after experiment with pieces of paper, cardboard, needles and punches. He used the idea of making raised dots on the paper from the underneath, but made up a new alphabet, an easier one than the one already used. After months and months of experimenting, his idea was ready to try out.

Louis showed the new alphabet to his teachers. They thought it was very good. They tried the new alphabet out by letting the blind people in the school use it. It worked. The people could write using a special pointed tool tool and a sort of metal ruler with blocks of six holes punched in it. As the pointed tool pushed through the holes in the 'ruler', it made dents in the paper. The paper could then be turned over and the blind person could feel the raised bumps and read what he or she had written. For the first time blind people could not only write, but could read back what they had written, or could read what someone else had written.

Louis Braille's idea for a new alphabet and writing tools quickly spread to other schools for blind people, and soon his method was used by people all over the world.

Today we call that method of reading and writing, Braille, after Louis Braille, its inventor. There are some books here, written in Braille that you might like to look at later. Remember that blind people read the books by feeling the dots with their fingers.*

Prayer

Dear God, thank you for our eyes with which we see to read and write.
Thank you for Louis Braille's invention which helps blind people
          to read and write.
Help us always to be considerate towards blind people,
          and to remember that apart from their eyes,
          they are people just like us.

Amen

Hymn
'He made me' **C&P**

*I showed the children a writing frame, equipment for writing in Braille, and a Braille book. All were loaned from the RNIB. On another occasion the school was visited by a representative from the RNIB who gave a most interesting talk and showed the children various aids for the blind. Local branches of the RNIB are usually happy to arrange such visits.

Christmas

There is a lovely feeling of excitement and anticipation in school at the moment: a feeling of excitement because of all the special things that are happening. Our school is beautifully decorated, there are tinselled trees, coloured lights, dancing mobiles and Christmas pictures in our classrooms, cloakrooms and hall. There are carols being sung, costumes being made, and concerts being practised, in every spare moment. There are parties being prepared, cards and presents being made, and all because of Christmas: celebrations because of a birthday, the birthday of a very special baby, nearly two thousand years ago.

Mary was going to have a baby. She knew her baby was going to be a special baby, she knew he was going to be a boy. Mary had a name already chosen for the baby, she would call him Jesus.

Mary lived in Nazareth, and was engaged to be married to Joseph, the village carpenter. One day as Mary and Joseph were talking together in Joseph's workshop, they heard a commotion in the market place. Joseph looked out of the doorway and saw some soldiers speaking to the villagers.

'It is a law passed by the Emperor Augustus', they said to the startled villagers, 'you have all to be counted. You must go back to the town of your birth, and report. You must set off this week to be counted', and the soldiers marched away to deliver the message to the people of the next village. Joseph and Mary went to join the crowd of people outside.

'What does it mean?' asked Joseph.

'It means what it says', answered one of the men. 'We must each go back to the town where we were born, to have our names entered on the census form. We have all to be counted.'

'But I come from Bethlehem, the City of David', said Jospeh. 'I can't go back there, it's too far, and what about Mary? The baby is due to be born soon.'

'You'll have to go', said the man. 'We all have to go. It's the law.' The people started to go home to prepare for the long journeys ahead.

The next day Joseph and Mary packed a few belongings into the donkey's saddle bags, and they set off for Bethlehem. It was a long journey. By the time they arrived in Bethlehem it was evening and they were both very, very tired. Mary was looking forward to finding a room at an inn, where she could lie down and sleep. She felt that her baby would be born very soon.

Joseph was surprised to see so many people in Bethlehem. He had not thought there would be so many to be registered here. The main street was crowded, and all the inns looked full. He knocked at the door of one.

'No room here, try down the road', said the red-faced innkeeper.

Joseph tried again.

'Sorry, we're full', said a woman.

Joseph tried again and again, but everywhere the answer was the same, 'Sorry. No room. Full.'

He turned away from the last inn, and saw tears in Mary's eyes. She was sad, frightened and unhappy.

'Just a minute', shouted the last innkeeper from his doorway. He too, had seen Mary's face. 'I've not a room in the house, but there's the stable;' he said, 'not much, but better than nothing. It's warm and dry. It'll take your donkey too.'

'Thank you', said Mary.

A few hours later, in the warm, dark, dry, safe stable, Mary's baby was born. She smiled at Joseph. They wrapped the baby warmly and put him in the animal's manger, because they did not have a cradle for him.

The world's special baby, Jesus, had arrived.

Later, the shepherds came to see the baby, and later still, Kings, bringing precious gifts of gold, frankincense and myrrh. And every year from then until now people remember and celebrate the very first Christmas.

Prayer

Once in Royal David's City
Stood a lowly cattle shed,
Where a mother laid her baby,
In a manger for his bed.
Thank you God, for that first Christmas,
Thank you, Lord, for Jesus Christ:
Help us all to give, this Christmas,
Happiness for Jesus Christ.

Amen

Hymn
'The Virgin Mary had a baby boy' **CGC**

Hanukkah
Week 11   Festivals

At this time of year, when Christian children are celebrating Christmas, Jewish children are celebrating a festival of lights, called Hanukkah. Each family has a special candlestick like this one,* called a menorah. It has eight candles which are all lit, one by one, from this servant candle in the middle. The festival lasts eight days; one day for each candle. Every day, when a

Hanukkah candle is lit, a Jewish boy or girl is given a present. Hanukkah is a happy festival; a time for playing games and singing, for visiting friends and giving gifts, especially gifts to the poor.

The very first Hanukkah was a happy occasion as well, but events leading up to it were far from happy. It all happened over two thousand years ago in the land of Israel. Soldiers marched into the country and seized the capital city. They ordered important Jewish people out of the city, they burnt Jewish temples and holy books, they even stole Jewish babies and took them up into the hills, where they left them to die. The Jewish people were very frightened and desperately unhappy.

One brave man called Judah the Maccabee, gathered together a small band of Jewish men, and they trained as warriors and began to fight back against the Syrian soldiers. At first the Maccabees were too weak to have any effect on the mighty Syrian army, but the Maccabees were brave and daring. They knew they were fighting for their land, their people and their lives. They knew they had to beat the Syrian army if they were to survive. The Maccabees knew the hills and mountains of Israel far better than the Syrian soldiers, and they raided the soldiers' camps at night, in the dark. The soldiers could not fight well in the dark because they didn't know the countryside as well as the Maccabees. Gradually the Maccabees began to win back small parts of their land.

One night, nearly three years after the fighting started, a great battle was fought at Emmaus, just outside Jerusalem. The Maccabees sprang suddenly upon the soldiers, sweeping down upon them from the hills. Many men were killed or injured, but the Maccabees surged on in battle into Jerusalem itself. Soon the Jewish people had won back their city and their land.

They set about cleaning the city and getting everything back to normal. They went into the temple and cleaned that. When all was set to rights again, they decided to hold a special service of dedication and thanksgiving in the temple. The Priest asked everyone to look for jars of holy oil, so that he could light the temple lamp – the menorah. All the jars of oil had been stolen or broken during the battles.

'There must be some jars of holy oil somewhere', said the Priest, 'please will everyone search. We must find some so that we can light our menorah, and begin our service. We cannot wait until new oil can be made from the olives, it will take eight days for the new oil to be ready.'

The people searched for jars of holy oil in all the places they thought jars might be hidden, but no oil could be found. Everyone's happiness at having their city back was beginning to turn into sadness. They so much wanted to hold their service of dedication, but it couldn't begin until the menorah was lighted.

Suddenly a small boy burst into the temple. 'I have found a jar of holy oil', he shouted. 'I think it is the last jar in the whole of Jerusalem.'

The people laughed and cheered and shouted, 'Let the service begin. Light the menorah.'

The Priest said, 'I will light the menorah but we have only one jar of oil. One jar will keep the menorah alight for only one day. The new oil will not be ready for another eight days.'

The Priest filled the lamp with the oil and lit the menorah. The service of dedication began. Afterwards the people celebrated, but they knew their celebrations could last only the one day, because the holy oil was enough only for one day.

The next morning, to everyone's surprise, the menorah was still lit. The Priest looked into the lamp; by now the oil should have been used and the lamp should be empty, but it was still full. 'It is a miracle', said the Priest. The people celebrated throughout the second day as well. On the third day the menorah was still burning. The people were astonished. 'It really *is* a miracle', they said, as they celebrated for the third day.

On the fourth, fifth, sixth, seventh and eighth days, the menorah steadily burned and glowed with light, all from the one jar of oil which should have

lasted only one day. On the eighth day, the new oil was ready, and by sunset on that day the menorah flame was spluttering and flickering as it used the last drop of the miraculous Hanukkah oil.

Ever since that time, Jewish people have celebrated eight days of Hanukkah, in memory of winning back their city, and of the holy oil which lasted for eight days.

Jewish people traditionally put their Hanukkah menorah in the window of their house so that everyone can see it. If you see a menorah you will know the story of the Hanukkah festival.

Prayer
Thank you, God, for festivals and happiness.
Help us to understand the festivals of other people.
Help us to know that everyone in the world
     belongs to the family of man.

Amen

Hymn
'Give me oil in my lamp' **C&P**

I brought a Hanukkah menorah in to show the children. If this is not possible to arrange, a picture or drawing could be shown to the children. I also put on display the book 'I am a Jew', published by Franklin Watts Ltd.

Diwali
Week 11   Festivals

This week we have been thinking about Festivals, and have heard about Christmas and Hanukkah. Both those festivals use lights; Christmas candles and lights on the tree, and Hanukkah candles in the menorah. A few weeks ago Hindu children were celebrating their festival of light, called Diwali. They light their homes with lamps, candles, sparklers and even indoor fireworks. The festival lasts for five days and reminds Hindus of the time, long ago, when Prince Rama returned to his kingdom after being away for fourteen years. The people of the forest all lit lamps to show him the way home through the darkness.

It all started when the King was searching for a husband for his beautiful daughter, Princess Sita. Many brave and handsome young men came forward to ask for Sita's hand in marriage, but the King made each young man take a test. He made each young man try to shoot an arrow from his magic bow. One by one the handsome young men failed the test, and went away sad and dejected.

One day Prince Rama came to the King's palace. He too lifted the King's magic bow. All eyes were on him as he pulled the bow-string back level with his shoulder. Further and further stretched the bow-string until, twang, the arrow sped sure and fast from the bow. Rama had passed the test. He was given the magic bow and the princess's hand in marriage. She was delighted to become the wife of the strong and handsome prince. Many people in the kingdom wished that Rama would be their next king, but one of the King's wives was jealous and angry because the people liked Rama.

'You must send Rama and Sita away', she said to the King. 'It is not right that Rama should be liked so much. You should send them far away for twice seven years. If the people still want them then, they should be allowed to return.'

The King was not happy to send Rama and Sita away, but he wanted to please his wife, so he agreed to the plan.

Rama and Sita left the luxury of the palace and went far away, deep into a forest, to live amongst the animals and the forest people. They were kind and considerate to everyone they met, and were soon well loved by the forest dwellers.

Each day when Rama went hunting for food, he drew a magic circle round the forest home, so that Sita would be safe until he returned. One dreadful day, the wicked, ugly, demon King Ravana came to the forest, and tricked Sita out of the magic circle. As soon as she was out of the circle's safety, Sita was kidnapped and hauled away to Ravana's kingdom beyond the sea. When Rama came home later that day, and found Sita gone, he was heart-broken. He searched through the forest for her, but there was no sign of where she might be, or what might have happened to her. As the long days dragged by, Rama became more and more unhappy in his loneliness.

One evening, as Rama sat in the doorway of his home, a large bird flew down to his feet. 'I have a message, Rama', said the bird. 'I have seen a beautiful princess held prisoner in the demon King Ravana's kingdom beyond the sea. She has asked me to tell you she is there.'

'Then she is alive', cried Rama, 'she is alive and I must rescue her. But how? I have no boat to cross the sea. I have no army to fight Ravana's demons.'

'We will help', said the monkeys were were listening in the trees of the forest. 'Come down to the sea.'

Rama picked up his magic bow and his arrows and followed the monkeys to the place where the sea meets the land. He fired one of his arrows into the sea and in the midst of the silvery splash of spray appeared a beautiful sea queen.

'I will help you', she said when she heard of Rama's problem. 'I will calm the sea and make the waves still so that you can build a pathway of stones to Ravana's island.'

The sea queen calmed the waves and the monkeys worked for hours to build a strong, stone pathway to the demon's island. As soon as the last stone was in place, Rama and the monkeys sped over the stones to confront Ravana and his demons. The demons were ready for battle and fiercely fought for their island. Rama pushed through the fighting and came face to face with Ravana. Rama silently lifted his magic bow, fitted an arrow, and drew back the string. Ravana fell, dead, at his feet. As soon as the demon army saw their King was dead, they turned and ran to hide on the island.

Rama quickly found Sita and together with the monkeys they crossed the stone pathway again, and returned to their forest home. The animals and forest people were pleased to have them back.

After fourteen years of living in their forest home, Rama and Sita decided to go back to the King's palace. All the forest people came out of their homes with lamps and lanterns, to light them safely on their way.

Rama and Sita arrived back safely to a wonderful welcome. Soon, Rama was made king, and Sita his queen, and everyone lived happily ever after.

Rama and Sita were liked and respected because they were kind, considerate and thoughtful to others. Rama was brave but gentle. Perhaps we can all learn something from the Hindu story.

Prayer

Thank you, God, for festivals of light and happiness.
Thank you for heroes who show the world good ways to be.
Help us all to spread happiness and lead good and useful lives.

Amen

Hymn

'When a knight won his spurs' **C&P**

Santa Claus   *Week 12   Christmas stories*

If I were to say to you 'What is the first thing you think of when I say "Christmas"?' I bet most of you would say 'presents'.

I can remember, when I was small, hardly being able to go to sleep on

Christmas Eve, because of excitement; wondering if I would be able to stay awake long enough to see Santa Claus: being afraid that if I did stay awake he might not come; worrying whether I really would get the presents I wanted so badly. I can remember waking up oh-so-early every Christmas Day morning and anxiously feeling the stocking at the bottom of my bed. One year I woke up so early that the stocking still hung there, limp and empty. A few hours later I woke again and it was fat and bulging, all out-of-shape with secret parcels.

Santa Claus is always so busy at Christmas-time, I don't suppose he ever stops to wonder about his ancestor Saint Nicholas. And I don't suppose Saint Nicholas ever thought that he would turn into Santa Claus, but legends tell us he did.

Nicholas was a young man, very kind, very good and very rich. He didn't care much about being rich, and thought it unfair that he had so much money when there were others who were very poor. He decided that he would give his money away to people who needed it, but he wouldn't let the people know that the money came from him, he would give it away secretly, so that they wouldn't know where it had come from.

One night when Nicholas was on his way home he passed a house and heard the sound of crying coming from inside. He stopped to listen. Inside the house was a father and his three daughters. The father had been a rich merchant, but had lost all his money in some foolish buying and selling. Now he had nothing and his daughters were to be sold as slaves and taken to countries far away across the sea. The girls were crying, because the next day the eldest girl was to be taken away from the family.

Nicholas hurried away from the house, went home and collected a bag of gold. Then, at midnight, in the darkness, he crept back to the merchant's house. Quietly he climbed up on to the low roof, and dropped the bag of gold down the chimney.

In the morning, the merchant and his daughters could hardly believe their eyes. The eldest daughter was saved, there was money enough now to pay the debtors, and she need not be sold as a slave.

If the merchant and his daughters were astonished that morning, they were absolutely amazed the next, when they discovered another bag of gold had been dropped down the chimney! Nicholas had visited the house again.

'Two bags of gold!' said the merchant. 'But three daughters. Surely it won't happen again tonight?' And he promised himself he would stay up all night to watch and to listen.

At midnight Nicholas came again. He had brought a third bag of gold for the third daughter. As quietly as he could Nicholas climbed again onto the low roof, and dropped a bag of gold down the chimney. As the bag hit the cold coals with a thud and a chink, the merchant jumped up and ran to the door. In the moonlight he saw Nicholas' long red cloak disappearing down the road.

'Ah, now I know who to thank', said the merchant to himself. 'The man is a Saint. He has saved our family. Tomorrow I will thank him.'

The next day the merchant searched the town for Nicholas, so that he could thank him for the kindness of the gifts, but Nicholas was nowhere to be found. In fact he was never seen again, but he still dropped gifts down the chimneys of people who needed help, and then he began to leave presents for children, always delivering them, whenever he could, down the family chimney.

Now he is known as Saint Nicholas, or Santa Claus for short.

I hope Santa Claus brings some exciting presents to your house this Christmas. Perhaps you could follow the example of Santa Claus' kindness and give something to someone who you know needs help, or a present to cheer them up.

Prayer

> Thank you, God, for the happiness of Christmas-time.
> Thank you for the gifts and presents we shall be given.
> Help us to do our best to help others,
>> especially those who need our help, following the
>> example of the young Saint Nicholas.

Amen

Hymn

> Stockings hanging by the fire
> Christmas lights shine bright
> Tinsel gleams from every house,
> Bells ring in the night,
> As we wait for Christmas Day,
> Let's remember, as we pray,
> All the hungry, homeless ones,
> On the earth tonight.

(words by I. Mawer)

Sung to the tune
'Look for signs that summer's done' **SSL**

The lop-sided Christmas tree

One of the things I like best about Christmas is the Christmas tree. Nowadays nearly every house and school and shop has a Christmas tree, and all different shapes and sizes. In Trafalgar Square in London, there is always a huge Christmas tree, a hundred feet tall, given to England by the people of Norway as a thank-you for help during the war. Most of the big shops in town have Christmas trees, some real and some artificial in gold, white and silver. I expect most of you have a Christmas tree in your home; I shall decorate my Christmas tree at home on the first day of the Christmas holiday, just as I do every year. Here in the hall is our school Christmas tree, that some of you helped me decorate a few days ago. It is a fir tree, now decorated with lights, baubles, tinsel, and a beautiful silver star.

There was once a fir tree, rather like this one, growing in a forest. It had a rather lop-sided look, because at one time its top-most branch had been damaged by snow, and the fir tree had needed to grow a new top branch at the side of the old one. The fir tree was teased by the other trees in the forest.

'You'll never be chosen,' they said, 'looking lop-sided like that. No, you'll not be chosen.'

He didn't know what it was he wouldn't be chosen for. He was too young to know what being a Christmas tree was all about, although he had heard some of the older trees talking about excitement and magic, coloured lights and decorations.

Having been told that he was too lop-sided to be chosen, made the fir tree feel very sad and lonely. He tried to stand as tall and straight as the others, but no matter how hard he tried, he still looked a little lop-sided.

One day there was great excitement in the forest. The woodcutters with their electric saws, tractors and trailers had arrived. The trees chosen to be Christmas trees were to be cut down and trimmed to make them look as handsome as possible. The woodcutters took down all the trees near the lop-sided fir tree; the men loaded them carefuly on to the trailers. The fir-tree knew they wouldn't choose him, but never-the-less his needles prickled with excitement as the men came near.

'This one's O.K. Sid', a voice shouted, and the fir tree quivered and tembled as the saw bit into his trunk. He too was carefully put onto the other trees on the trailer.

'There must be some mistake.'

'He's not tall and straight like us.'

'He's lop-sided', murmured the whispering voices of the trees, but the fir tree didn't care. He was here, being bumped and jolted along the road with the others; he was chosen to be included in the trailerload of trees; his was to be the excitement of Christmas.

The trees were delivered to a garden centre, and, almost as quickly as they were unloaded, they were sold; one to a house, one to a factory, one to a hospital; all to be Christmas trees. All, that is, except the lop-sided fir tree. He was left leaning lop-sidedly against the fence. Snow began to fall on him, he felt wretched.

Late that evening came a man, hurrying, wanting a Christmas tree, quickly.

'That looks the right size and shape', he said. 'Yes, that one looks fine. I'll take it now, please.'

The fir tree could hardly believe his ears. The garden centre man explained about the lop-sided top, but the other man said, 'It's perfect.'

Perfect. Just think.

The man took the lop-sided fir tree, and put it in a pot in a huge, cold hall. He decorated the tree with fairy lights, twinkling, sparkling, coloured balls, and glistening silver tinsel. Then he turned out all the lights and left. The tree stood in its shimmering beauty, hardly daring to breath lest a sliver of silver should fall. He waited and waited and waited. He stood perfectly still for two whole days. Nothing happened. Was this Christmas? thought the tree. Was this what all the excitement had been about, this cold, lonely, silent wait? Was this it?

On the third day he heard a noise, footsteps, a shout, a laugh, voices, lots of voices; and into the hall came the children, hundreds of children, laughing, smiling, pointing, oohing, and aahing.

'Isn't it lovely', they said. 'It's beautiful. It's the best Christmas tree ever. Look at its lights, its tinsel, its decorations, its star. It's wonderful', they said. The tree glowed with pride and happiness, it's lop-sided branch forgotten. Now he knew. Now he understood how special it was to be a Christmas tree in a school.

For the next few days he shone and shimmered in the centre of all the excitement. The children sat round him, sang carols near him, and he heard the story of the first Christmas. He was pleased to share in that warm, happy atmosphere, and to take part in the magical excitement of Christmas.

Prayer

Thank you, God, for Christmas trees.
Thank you for the happiness and joy they bring us.
Help us to share that happiness with others.

Amen

Hymn
'O Christmas tree' **CGC**

Good King Wenceslas *Week 12 Christmas stories*

I have just about finished my Christmas shopping. The hardest part of buying Christmas presents is deciding what to buy, choosing the right present for each person. There is a saying which goes, 'It's the thought that counts', which I think is true. It is easy to go to the shops and simply buy the first thing you see, for your mum or your dad or your brother or sister or aunt. It is much harder to really think about the person, to think of their hobbies and interests, to think of a present that they would really like. Sometimes grown-ups like to be given a home-made present, because that often shows that you've given a great deal of thought and time to making it for them.

Sometimes you can give a lot of happiness to someone, by giving them an unexpected small gift. Then the present is a double surprise, because of the present itself, and because it wasn't expected.

A long time ago, a king gave an unexpected present to a poor man he hardly knew. King Wenceslas was looking out of his palace window one bitterly cold, snowy night. The King was warm and comfortable in the palace. He had just eaten a delicious dinner, and he was feeling happy. Outside, the snow was deep, the lake was frozen, and the moon shone on the white icy world. The King was just about to turn away from his window, when he a movement outside. He looked more closely, and there in the distance, he could see a man in poor, ragged clothing trudging through the snow and every so often bending down to pick something up from the frozen ground. King Wenceslas could see that the man was collecting firewood. He had already gathered a small bundle of sticks and these were tied together and being carried on the man's shoulder.

'He'll not gather much useful firewood tonight', thought the King. 'Most of it is hidden under the snow, and the bit there is to be seen is sodden, too wet to be of use to anyone.'

The King turned away from the window and called for his servant boy. 'Do you know that man over there?' he asked.

'Yes, I know him', answered the boy. 'He and his wife live in the cottage at the side of the mountain. I don't think they have much money. The man does odd jobs for people, when he can get the work.'

'There'll not be much work at this time of year,' said the King, 'and they'll not be having a very good Christmas, I'll be bound. Come on boy, we'll alter that! We'll give them a Christmas to remember.'

The King sent the servant boy to the kitchen for food, to the cellar for wine and to the yard for logs. They packed the things together in bags and boxes, put on their cloaks and boots and set off into the cold dark night. The wind whistled round their ears and blew flurries of snow into their faces. The King's hands were cold and the boy's feet were wet, but neither of them complained or grumbled. They plodded on through snow that grew deeper and deeper every minute. The boy grew colder, his parcels grew heavier and his feet sank deeper and deeper into the snow until he felt he could go no further. He called to the King.

'It's harder for you', said the King, 'you're smaller than me. Look! You walk behind me, I'll shelter you a bit from the wind and storm, and you can put your feet in my footprints then you'll not sink quite so deeply. Come on. Not far now.'

The boy found it easier, walking behind in the King's footsteps. Soon they arrived at the poor man's cottage. He had just arrived home with his bundle of sticks, and was astonished to see the King on his doorstep. The King said 'Happy Christmas', and gave the man his present of food, wine and logs.

The man said, 'And a Happy Christmas to you too, Sir. Thank you. It's a Christmas to remember.'

King Wenceslas shared some of what he had, to make someone else happy. Perhaps we can all try to share something that we have, to try and make another person happy this Christmas.

Prayer

Dear God, thank you for Christmas.
Thank you for all the lovely things we will have this holiday.
Please help everyone, all over the world,
            to have some happiness this Christmas.

Amen

Hymn
'Good King Wenceslas' **OBC**

Spring Term

Happy New Year

This morning I am not going to say 'Good morning' to you. I am going to say something else. Let's see if you can give me the right answer.

'Happy New Year, everyone.'

(*response from children*)

This is our first assembly of this year. The New Year began on January 1st, and so today, January 8th we are eight days into the new year.

When the year is new, all of it stretches ahead into the future, 12 months, 52 weeks, and 365 days. We don't know what is going to happen during this year, because we cannot look into the future. But we do know that this new year, like all new years, holds within it the *promise* of being good and happy. However, the new year cannot fulfil the promise by itself. We need to help it by being kind, cheerful, helpful and thoughtful; by sharing and by trying to do our best in all we do.

The New Year with its promise that needs help is like one of my Christmas presents.*

One of my friends who knows I like gardening bought me this box for Christmas. The box says 'scented garden', but I didn't understand how such a small box could contain a garden. I opened the box carefully and inside found a plastic propagator – that's a container like a tiny greenhouse – some growing compost, and six tiny envelopes. What do you think is inside the envelopes? Yes, they each contain different kinds of seeds. In the Spring I need to put compost into the six compartments of the propagator, sow the seeds, water them, and put them in a dark, warm place until they begin to grow. Then, when the tiny shoots start to appear, I will need to give them warmth and light, and I will need to remember to water them. If I look after the tiny plants carefully, and help them to grow, I will be able to plant them out in my garden in the summer. Then they will grow into strong plants and they will flower. All these flowers have a lovely perfume – that's why the box is called the 'scented garden'.

The box as it is holds a promise, but the plants won't grow on their own, if I just leave them in there. I need to help them along.

The scented garden is like the New Year. They both hold a promise, but they need help from us to fulfil that promise. Let us all work together in our school to make this New Year into a good new year.

Prayer

Dear God, thank you for the New Year.
Thank you for the promise of happiness and good things
       that each new year holds.
Help us to help that promise grow.
Help us to help to make this year a happy year.

Amen

Hymn

'One more step along the world I go' **C&P**

*I brought in to assembly a boxed gardening kit containing propagator, compost, seeds etc. This I opened and unpacked at the beginning of the 'story'. If a kit is unavailable, a homemade pack containing pot(s), compost and packeted seeds would do equally well.

Resolutions

Week 1   New Year

We have already heard this week that the new year holds a promise but that we must help that promise along. Sometimes people make themselves a promise in the new year to try harder, or to do something better than before. The new year is a good time for people to look carefully at themselves to see if there is anything that needs improving, to see if there is anything that is not as good as it might be. The new year is a good time to make a promise to put those things right. We call these personal promises at this time of year – New Year resolutions.

Here is a story about someone who made a New Year resolution, and who tried hard to keep the resolution once it was made.

It all started on the 1st of December when the King was given an early Christmas present of a box of chocolates. He was very partial to sweets and chocolates and buns and biscuits, so he was very pleased with the present.

'I think I'll not have dinner today', he said. 'I'll have these chocolates instead.' He sent a message to the royal kitchen for the cook not to bother with dinner for the King that day.

The next day, someone gave the King a tin of biscuits as an early Christmas box.

'Mmm, thank you', said the King. 'I think I'll not bother with tea today, I'll just eat my biscuits.'

On the third day, with all his chocolates and biscuits eaten, the King decided to ask the cook to make him a huge mince pie. 'I'll have it instead of my ordinary meals', he said.

On the fourth day, someone gave the King a large iced Christmas cake and a 'selection' box.

'Mmmm', said the King. 'Forget about dinner, cook, I'll just eat these.'

On the fifth day, the King ate a whole tin of toffees instead of breakfast, a tin of shortbread instead of his dinner, and three boxes of After Eights for his tea.

And so it went on, all through December. The King ate more and more sweets, chocolates and biscuits, and fewer and fewer proper meals. Before much longer he was beginning to look quite ill. He was getting fatter, his cheeks sagged and his eyes looked dull. His teeth ached, his skin looked yellow and he was tired, irritable and bad-tempered with everyone. He no longer bothered to try to help his people, as he had done earlier. Everyone began to worry about him, but he would not eat proper meals, and he would not stop eating sugary things.

On Christmas Day itself the King was ill all day, and did not enjoy himself one bit.

'You'll have to stop eating all these sweets', said the Queen, 'or you'll die.'

'Yes, I know', said the King, 'but I can't, I can't.'

'I can help you', said a tiny old man from the back of the room, 'If you'll come and stay with me for a few days.'

So the Queen packed a bag, and the King went to stay in the old man's cottage.

On his first morning in the cottage, the King woke up to the delicious smell of bacon and eggs. 'Scrumptious', he said. 'I've almost forgotten how good bacon and eggs can be. I'm really looking forward to my breakfast.' He quickly dressed and went to the kitchen, where the old man was taking sizzling crisp bacon out of the pan.

'Hello', said the man, 'here's your breakfast. I hope you're ready for it.' He handed the King a plate of chocolate biscuits, and ate the delicious bacon and eggs himself.

'Oh!' said the King. 'I thought the bacon and eggs were for me!'

'Oh no', replied the man, 'you like chocolate don't you? So the biscuits are for you.'

The King was disappointed, but he didn't want to complain, and he *did* like chocolate biscuits, so he ate them all up.

During the morning the man made a tasty beef casserole with dumplings. The rich smells of gravy, onions, carrots, pepper and sage wafted to the King's nostrils.

'I'm looking forward to my dinner', he said to the man.

'Good! I have a lovely plate of turkish delight for you. I'm going to have the beef stew', said the man.

'Oh!' said the King. 'I thought the beef was for me!'

'Oh no', said the man, 'the chocolate-covered turkish delight is for you.'

The King was disappointed, but he didn't want to complain, so he ate up all the turkish delight.

At tea-time the man cooked fish, and ate it whilst the King struggled to eat a bowl of chopped up Mars bars. At suppertime, he couldn't face the dish of pink candyfloss that the old man gave him.

At bedtime, the King said, 'I think I'd like to go home please, I don't feel well. I think I've been very silly.'

'I think you have', said the old man.

'I shall make a resolution to do better in the New Year', promised the King.

For the next few days the King ate very little because he felt so ill. At the beginning of the New Year he tried hard to eat proper meals and far fewer sweets and slowly his handsome good looks and all his energy returned, and he was once again a helpful King to his people.

We are not as greedy as that King, but there may be something about us that we could try to make better this New Year. There may be something that we could resolve to improve. Perhaps we could make a resolution that would not just improve ourselves, but that would help make our school better.

Prayer

Dear God, Help us to do what we can to improve what we can;
and do what we can at our best.

Amen

Hymn

'Give me oil in my lamp' **C&P**

Spanish oranges
Week 1   New Year

In our last assembly, we thought about making promises, or New Year Resolutions, and I asked if you could think of a resolution that might help everyone in our school. One person suggested that we could promise to share things with each other, and that sharing could make us happier. It's quite easy to share things like sweets, or toys or games, but perhaps we could try to work together to share our time, talents and happiness as well. Today's story is about a lady who felt so happy she wanted to share her happiness with her friends and family, but at first she couldn't think how to do it.

Mr and Mrs Kershaw had gone on holiday in the summer to Spain. Mrs Kershaw had never been in a plane before and had been very excited about going. Usually they went on holiday to the seaside with their children and grandchildren, but this year Mr Kershaw's holiday from work wasn't at the same time as the school holidays and so they couldn't go on holiday all together.

Mr and Mrs Kershaw had carefully chosen a hotel to stay in, from the holiday brochure, and at last they were there.

'Oh, this is lovely', said Mrs Kershaw, 'it's just like the photographs in the brochure, but better. There's everything here we could want. There's warm sunshine, delicious food, nice people to meet, beautiful gardens, lovely shops, a swimming pool with comfy chairs all round . . . ooh it's lovely. I just wish we could share it with all our friends and family at home.'

'Well, we can't bring them all out here', said Mr Kershaw.

'No, I don't suppose we can', said his wife, 'but I wish we could.'

The lovely long summer days followed each other, each one better than the last; and hardly a day went by without Mrs Kershaw saying, 'Oh, I'm having such a nice holiday, I wish we could share it with everyone at home.' But, of course there wasn't a way of sharing the holiday with everyone at home.

Soon, too soon it seemed, it was almost time for the holiday to be over. On the last morning, Mrs Kershaw did some shopping in the market, and bought some presents for the family. Just as she was leaving the market, she bought a big bag of Spanish oranges from the greengrocery stall. Then it was time to go back to the hotel and pack and catch the coach and plane back home.

After a few days back at home the holiday seemed a long way away. The presents had been given away, the photographs had been carefully put in the album, and all that was left were the happy memories – and the bag of Spanish oranges, now sitting in Mrs Kershaw's kitchen.

'Even they're looking a bit wizened now', thought Mrs Kershaw. 'They need throwing out.' She was just about to put them in the bin when she had an idea.

She went not to the bin, but to the garage, and got a plant pot and some compost, and took them back to the kitchen. Very carefully she cut each orange in half and took out the pips. Very gently she put each pip into the plant pot full of soil. She watered the plant pot, put it in a plastic bag, and put the whole thing in the airing cupboard. Then she waited . . . and waited . . . and waited, and each day just checked the plant pot in the airing cupboard. After a long wait, she finally saw what she had been waiting for – one tiny shoot beginning to push its way out of the soil. She gave the plant pot a little more water, and put it back in its warm dark airing cupboard for a few more days. More tiny shoots began to grow. Mrs Kershaw then put the plant pot on her warm sunny windowsill and carefully watered it when it became dry. The tiny shoots grew and turned green. Leaves appeared, and soon the small plants were big enough to go into pots of their own. Still Mrs Kershaw kept them on her window sill, and looked after them carefully. Weeks passed and the plants grew bigger and stronger. Just before Christmas time, each tiny tree needed a bigger pot, and in the New Year, Mrs Kershaw was able to give all her friends and relatives a present of a small, but growing orange tree.

'In a way, I did share my holiday with everyone', she said.

Perhaps, this New Year, we can make an extra effort to share our happiness together.

Prayer
> Dear God, Please help us, this New Year,
>> to share what we can do with others.
> Help us to share not just our toys or our sweets,
>> but our time, our talents and our happiness.

Amen

Hymn
'The family of man' **C&P**

The builders   *Week 2   Working together*

Last week we talked about sharing – not just our 'things', but our time, our skills and our happiness. At school we often have the greatest success when we work together: our football team can only do well if all the players work together; our choir only sounds good when everyone in it sings together. Sometimes we work together on projects, or making music, or doing a class assembly. All these times are best when everyone joins together and co-operates. Our school needs the help of everyone in our school family from the oldest to the youngest. We all have an important job to do and we are all good at something.

Once upon a time there was a bear, a monkey and a fox who were good friends. They all lived near to each other, in the forest, and often popped into each others' houses. One day they were in the bear's house, having a cup of tea and a chat, and they started to talk about their homes.

'Well, I'm thinking of building a new house', said the bear. 'This one is a bit tumbledown. I'd like a lovely, new, modern house.'

'It's funny you should say that', said the fox. 'I've been thinking just the same thing. I could do with a new house as well.'

'Well, what about mine!' added the monkey. 'My house nearly falls down every time the wind blows. I certainly need a new one.'

'We will each build ourself a new house', decided the bear. 'It shouldn't take us long if we work hard.'

So each animal set to work, collecting together the things he would need. They knew what had happened to the three little pigs, so they knew they needed strong building materials like bricks and stones, wood, cement and sand, if the houses were to be safe and strong.

The bear started digging out the foundations of his house. He was big and strong and found this part easy. He carried piles of bricks in a hod and in no time had built his house up to the roof. He hoisted the huge wooden rafters into place.

Meanwhile the monkey was still struggling with the foundations. He wasn't as big as the bear and couldn't dig and carry heavy weights as easily. He found it all very difficult.

The fox wasn't managing much better either. He was even smaller than the monkey and not as strong. He soon gave up trying to dig and lay bricks, and spent his time writing down complicated measurements on a piece of paper.

The bear by now had finished his roof and he sat up there watching the monkey and the fox struggling to build their houses.

'They're not getting on very fast', he said. The bear climbed down from the roof and began the work on the inside of his house. He had to carefully bend and fit water pipes and fasten them to the taps on his sink. He had to thread wires for the electricity through the house, and fasten them to the wall sockets with tiny gold screws. He suddenly discovered that he couldn't do these small careful jobs. His big paws that had helped him get on so quickly when he was digging and building, were no good for fiddly jobs like fastening on tiny gold screws. He sat on the floor and sadly put his head in his paws. 'I'm stuck', he said.

By now, the monkey and the fox had given up their building, (it was much too hard for them), and they had come along to see how the bear was getting along. Of course they found out that he was stuck as well.

'It should have worked', moaned the bear. 'We should have been able to build ourselves new houses.'

'I could have easily fixed the wires and the pipes, if only I'd been able to build the walls', said the monkey.

'I had written my plans downs', grumbled the fox. 'I could have built my house if I'd had a bit of help.'

'That's it!' shouted the bear. 'That's where we've gone wrong. We needed to work together and help each other. We're each good at doing the jobs that others can't do. We can build our new houses if we work together.'

And that's exactly what they did. In a short time the bear, the ~~monkey~~ <ins>hare</ins> and the fox each had a brand-new, beautifully built house, in which to live.

We can achieve much more in our school <ins>families</ins> when we work together and work as a team, because we are all good at something. <ins>And God has given all things we can do because we are part of his family</ins>

Prayer
> Many hands build a building,
> Many hearts make a school. <ins>see over for prayer</ins>
> Help us, Lord, to work together to make our school
> a good place to be.
>
> *Amen*

Hymn
'The building song' **C&P**

Joey Deacon

Week 2 Working together

Today I have a story about four men, who, like the animals in our last assembly story, worked together. But, today's story is a true story. These four men really lived, and everything in the story really happened.

It all started when Mrs Deacon had another baby boy. She was very happy, and decided to call the new baby Joey.

One day, when Joey lay in her arms, Mrs Deacon looked down at him and noticed that his tiny fingers, and his legs didn't seem to be moving properly. She also noticed that he wasn't feeding as easily as her other children had done. As the days passed she became more sure something was wrong. She took Joey to the doctor, who said he must go to hospital to have some tests. By now, Mrs Deacon was very worried about Joey. In the hospital, the doctors gently told her that there was something wrong with Joey; that the part of his brain which controlled Joey's muscles wasn't working properly, and that they were sorry, but he would never be able to walk, or to use his hands properly, or even talk, and that there wasn't really anything they could do. Mrs Deacon felt very upset, and then she felt very angry. 'There will be something that Joey can do', she said. 'Just you wait and see. He'll be good at something, because everyone is good at something.'

Mrs Deacon took Joey home, and looked after him, and talked to him and tried to teach him to do things, but there didn't seem to be anything that Joey could do. Months went by and the time came for Joey to start school, but he wasn't able to go, because he couldn't use his arms or legs properly and he couldn't talk.

One day Mrs Deacon talked to Joey about the cars parked outside; there were four cars and Joey blinked his eyes four times. Mrs Deacon was astonished. 'How many trees are there Joey?' she asked. There were six trees, Joey blinked his eyes six times. 'I was right', shouted Mrs Deacon. 'There is something he can do, Joey can think! I knew he would be good at something.' From then on Mrs Deacon learned to understand Joey's strange sounds and movements, and Joey was happy that his mother could understand him.

Many years later, Mrs Deacon became ill, and sadly she died. Joey's auntie and grandma and his dad looked after him, but they couldn't understand what he tried to say to them, and Joey became difficult because he missed his mum so much. A little later, Joey's dad died as well, and his auntie and grandma could not look after him any more. By now Joey was a man and they decided that it would be best if Joey went to live in a special hospital where doctors and nurses could look after him properly, and so Joey was moved to the hospital.

The nurses looked after him well and cared for him, but they were very busy and didn't have time to learn what Joey's strange sounds meant, and so once again there was no-one to understand him, and Joey became very unhappy. Also staying in the hospital was a man called Ernie, who was handicapped. Now everyone is good at something, and Ernie was a very patient man and was good at watching and listening. He had something the nurses didn't have, he had lots of spare time, and he used to spend so long staring at Joey, and listening to the sounds that he made, that before long Ernie was able to do what Joey's mum had been able to do, he could understand Joey. At last Joey had a friend, who could understand him, and in his own way he could talk to his friend. Joey and Ernie had two more friends; Michael, who was the only person in the hospital apart from the doctors and nurses, who could read and write, and Tom, who had an old typewriter, and although he couldn't read or write, he could copy words, with one finger, on his typewriter. At last Joey felt happy, and then one more bit of bad luck came along. Joey became ill, there was something wrong with his lungs and he couldn't breathe properly. Joey was sent to another hospital away from his friends.

Joey became so unhappy he didn't even try to get better. One day he lay in his bed watching the man in the next bed writing a story. 'I wish I could write', thought Joey. 'I wish I could write all about me, and tell everyone what it's like to be handicapped, but I can't hold a pencil or use a typewriter like Tom.' Then he had an idea! 'I *could* write my story! I could do it, but

I need to be back in my old hospital with my friends.' And from that moment Joey began to get better. Soon he was well enough to go back to join Ernie, Michael and Tom. They were all very pleased to see each other. Joey used his sounds and signs to tell his plan to Ernie, who told it to the others, and they began straight away to write Joey's story.

Joey made Ernie understand the story. Ernie told Michael what Joey had said. Michael wrote it down with pencil and paper. Tom copied the writing onto his typewriter. And in this way, the four friends wrote a whole book.

It took them a long time; one whole day to write just four lines, and the whole book took fifteen years to write, but, together, they did it.

None of those men could have written the book by themselves, but together they were able to do it.

If four handicapped men could write a book, just think of the exciting things we in our school could do by working together.

Prayer
Dear God, Please help us to know that everyone is good at something.
Help us to share our talents and work together.
Help us to work together in our homes and in our school and
help our families and our friends.

Amen

Hymn
'Join with us' **C&P**

The bird-catcher and the quails
Week 2   Working together
adapted from the Sammodamāna-Jātaka

When we do something together it is important that we all join in to help. Sometimes people argue or quarrel about helping and when that happens nothing seems to go right. Some small brown birds argued in today's story. As soon as they started to argue, they stopped helping each other and then something dreadful happened.

Once upon a time when Brahmadatta was King of Benares, the Bodhisatta (who was a very wise one) was born as a quail and lived in the forest with a thousand other quails.

Nearby, lived a bird-catcher. He used to crouch in the bushes and wait for a flock of birds to settle on the ground. Then he would jump up, throw a net over them, gather up the edges with the birds in the middle, stuff them all in his basket, and take them off to market to sell, before the birds had time even to utter a cheep of protest.

The Bodhisatta (who remember was a very wise one) said to the rest of the quails, 'If we all work together we can save ourselves. Next time the net falls on some of us, we must poke our heads throught the mesh and then all beat our wings together. We will carry the net to a thorn bush and land in its branches. The net will become tangled in the thorns and we can escape from under it.'

'What a good idea', shouted the birds. 'We will work together to save ourselves.'

The next day when the bird-catcher threw his net over a group of quails, he was astonished to see the net carried up in the air over to a thorn bush, and the birds escape from underneath it.

'Well! I never saw anything like it', said the bird-catcher to himself as he untangled his net from the thorns.

The next day, the same thing happened again and the bird-catcher went home without a single quail for market.

The following day, the same thing happened again. The next day and the next and the next, the birds escaped by carrying the net to a nearby thorn bush.

On the seventh day the bird-catcher's wife grew angry. 'What are you going to do about it?' she shouted. 'You're letting the birds fool you. When are you going to find another way to catch them?'

'Oh, there's no need to find another way', answered the birdcatcher. 'Their plan is working now, but just be patient. Soon they will argue amongst themselves and then their plan won't work.'

Sure enough, the very next day, the quails started to argue. One of the quails accidentally trod on the foot of another.

'Who trod on my foot?' snapped the quail.

'It wasn't me', said one.

'It wasn't me', answered another.

'It was you', shouted the first quail, pecking one of them with his beak.

'No it was not. Who are you pecking? Go away.'

'Don't you tell me to go away. Who do you think you are? You need me to help lift the net'.

'I don't need you. I can lift the net without your help'.

'No you can't'.

'Yes I can'.

'I'm the best at lifting the net', shouted another.

'You're not. I'm the strongest', boasted one more.

Whilst all the quails were quarrelling and arguing, the bird-catcher threw the net over them all, gathered up the edges with the birds in the middle, and stuffed them in his basket.

'Got you', he shouted. 'That'll teach you to argue amongst yourselves', and he took the birds to market.

The Bodhisatta (who remember was a very wise one) thought 'there's no safety with those who quarrel. I'm leaving' and he left to go and live somewhere else.

Sometimes people in school quarrel like the quails. When that happens it's sad because it means people are working against each other instead of working with each other to make our school a happy, busy place. Let's try to remember that things work best when we all co-operate and work together.

Prayer

Please God, help us to care about each other.
Help us to share with each other.
Help us to work together and to remember that everyone
from the biggest to the smallest has a part to play in our school.

Amen

Hymn
'Tomorrow' **SFJ**

Mrs Smith
Week 3   Feed the birds

On Sunday evening, as I was driving home in my car, I noticed an animal moving in a gateway at the side of the road. The animal came out of the gateway, crossed the grass verge, ran across the road, and disappeared into some gardens at the other side. At first I thought it was a cat. Then I realised the animal was too big for a cat; I thought it must be a dog. It was small, dog-shaped, but had a long bushy tail. It was a fox.

The fox must have moved out of its usual living place in the woods and fields, and come near to the houses for food. In cold winter weather many animals and birds find it hard to get the food and water they need, because the ground is hard and frozen. The birds, especially, need our help at this time of year, to stay alive.

I have a bird table in my garden, and in winter, I try hard each day to remember to put left-over scraps of food out for them.

There was once a lady called Mrs Smith, who had a bird table in her garden; she tried to remember to feed the birds in winter time. One particular weekend, the weather became bitterly cold, and it snowed all Sunday. On Monday morning Mrs Smith got up and got ready to go to work. She looked out of her window and saw the bird table all covered with snow, and the bird's water dish solid with ice. 'I must remember to feed the birds', she thought. 'They'll be hungry. I'll do it later.' But somehow, Mrs Smith didn't find the time to put out any food or water.

On Tuesday, when Mrs Smith got up, she saw even more snow. It had snowed all through the night, and before she could set off for work, she had to clear her drive of snow, and dig it away from the front of the garage. She had no time to feed the birds that day.

On Wednesday, Mrs Smith simply forgot to put any food out. By the time she remembered it was early evening; it was dark, and all the birds were sheltering for the night. 'I must remember to feed them tomorrow', she said.

On Thursday morning, Mrs Smith was late up. Something must have gone wrong with the alarm clock, or perhaps it did ring and she went back to sleep again. Anyway, she had only a few minutes in which to get ready, have her breakfast, and set off in her car to work. There was no time to feed the birds.

When Mrs Smith woke up on Friday morning, it was wilder than ever. She shivered as she put her feet into her slippers and went into the bathroom. From the window she could see her garden. It was quiet and icy cold. A bitter wind was blowing flurries of snow around the bird table.

'Brrr! It's too cold to stand out there this morning', thought Mrs Smith. 'I'll wait until tomorrow to put some food out for the birds. It'll be better to wait. Tomorrow is Saturday. I won't have to go to work, and I'll have more time.' So, the birds had no food on Friday.

On Saturday, Mrs Smith got up, and went downstairs into her kitchen. She was standing looking out of her window, wondering what scraps she could put out for the birds, when she saw something brown on the ground at the bottom of the bird table. 'What's that?' she said. 'I bet it's that brown glove I lost last week; or perhaps it's that small leather purse I lost.' She put on her coat and went outside to look. She bent down and carefully picked it up. Gently cupped in her hands was a small, cold, ruffle-feathered robin. Its beak was frosted tightly shut, it had a dusting of snow on its brown and red body. It was dead.

Well, you can imagine how sad Mrs Smith felt. 'Oh dear! If only I'd tried harder during the week to feed the birds, perhaps this robin wouldn't have died', she said. 'Well, I'll try to help the rest of the birds.' And Mrs Smith went back into her kitchen and made a bird-cake. Every day during the next week she remembered to put a piece of the bird-cake onto her birdtable. *

Of course, it wasn't altogether Mrs Smith's fault that the robin died. Sadly, many birds die in the cold winter months, but if we remember to put out food for them, we shall help many birds to stay alive, that might otherwise die.

Prayer

Thank you, God, for birds: for their cheerful presence
    and their happy song.
Help us to remember to feed the birds in winter,
    when it is hard for them to find food for themselves.

Amen

Hymn

'Who put the colours in the rainbow' **C&P**

*At this point the children and I discussed various foods which can be put out for birds. I showed them some commercial peanut dispensers, and together we made 'Mrs Smith's birdcake'. I had several containers of food on the table, cornflakes, biscuits, raisins, oats, nuts (shelled), bacon rind etc, and chose one child per container to come out and say what the container held. We then mixed spoonfuls of ingredients in a pyrex basin, and called on an adult (member of staff) to collect the pre-arranged jug of melted lard from the school kitchen (in our case adjacent to hall). The fat was poured on to the mixture and left for the remainder of the day to cool and harden. We turned it out in the following assembly and noted how the lard had solidified on cooling. The 'cake' was then broken up and put out for the 'school' birds.

Speckleboss
Week 3   Feed the birds

Yesterday we made a birdcake like the one Mrs Smith made in the story. Yesterday the hot fat in this basin was liquid, today you can see as I turn the basin upside down, that it has set white and hard. The fat is holding together all the food. I'll turn it out and you will see that it will keep its shape. Now we can cut pieces from the cake and put them outside for our birds.

When Mrs Smith put her bird cake on the birdtable in her garden, she immediately found that she had a problem! The smaller birds, like the sparrows were not able to eat any of the food, because as soon as the bigger birds saw food on the bird table they swooped down, squabbling and fighting, and chased the smaller birds away. At first Mrs Smith simply left the birds to it, thinking, 'Well, they'll sort it out for themselves', and she got on with her jobs inside the house.

Every now and then she went to the window to look out, and each time she looked out, she saw the same thing. Near her window, between the house and the bird table, was a bush, on which the smaller birds sat, queuing up, while they waited for a chance to fly to the bird table. There were sparrows, blue-tits and great-tits, a chaffinch and a robin. Behind the bird table, in the garden next door, was a wooden shed, and on the roof of the shed sat some starlings, one of them had ragged feathers and was bigger than all the rest. Mrs Smith called him 'Speckleboss'. It seemed as though Speckleboss waited until the small birds were eating at the bird table, then he squawked to the other starlings, and down they all flew in a flurry, scattering small birds and food all over the ground. In no time the little birds were hiding in fear, and the starlings were eating their fill. Then the starlings would fly back to the shed roof, the small birds would cautiously come out of their hiding places, they would queue up in the bush ready to fly to the bird table, and the whole performance would start all over again.

'Well, this is no good', said Mrs Smith to herself. 'I'll have to do something about this, or those small birds will never have anything to eat.' She remembered a book about gardening and wild birds that her friend had given her last Christmas, so she got it out of her bookshelf, sat down in her chair, and read it to see if she could find an answer to her problem.

'Large birds may keep smaller birds away when feeding,' she read, 'so put out different food in separate places, so that more birds can feed at one time.'

'Now, why didn't I think of that?' Mrs Smith asked herself. 'I'll try it and see if it works.' Mrs Smith went to her kitchen and collected some biscuit crumbs, some bacon rind cut into small pieces, and an apple. She threw all that food on her lawn. Sure enough, the starlings led by Speckleboss, swooped down from the shed roof. Soon a blackbird and a thrush joined Speckleboss and his friends. Then Mrs Smith went back inside for a piece of birdcake, which she broke up and put on the birdtable. The large birds stayed on the lawn with their food, and the sparrows, blue-tits, great-tits, chaffinch and robin all queued up in the bush and ate from the birdtable. All the birds were able to have something to eat.

'There,' said Mrs Smith, 'that's what I'll do every day, and then it will be fair for all the birds, and Speckleboss won't have it all his own way!'

It will be helpful if we remember that some birds, like the thrushes, like to eat from the ground, and that other birds, like the sparrows and blue-tits, will happily eat from a birdtable. If we can put out different food, in different places, we will be able to help and keep many birds alive. Remember that birds like not just bread, but bones, cheese, porridge oats, nuts, bacon rind, currants, apples and baked potatoes; and all birds need water for drinking and bathing.

Prayer

Thank you, God, for the food we eat.
Help us to help the birds stay alive in wintertime,
    by putting out food for them.
Help us to help the birds stay alive in wintertime,
    by giving them fresh water, and replacing it
    when it becomes frozen.

Amen

Hymn

'Little birds in winter time' **SSL**

The Jones' boy and the canary   *Week 3   Feed the birds*

This week we have been thinking about helping the birds, and keeping them alive during the cold winter weather. However, there have been times when birds have helped to save the lives of men.

You may not think it possible that something as small as a bird could save the life of a man, but it really happened.

There was a family called Jones; Mr and Mrs Jones, and their four sons, Ivan, David, Dylan and Morgan. The family lived in a village in South Wales, and Mr Jones, Ivan, David, Dylan and Morgan were all coal-miners, like all the men of the village.

Early every morning, Mrs Jones packed up five 'snap' boxes – tin boxes containing their lunch – and the five men set off down the village street, clattering on the cobbles in their clogs, and meeting other miners, all on their way to the early shift at the pit.

First the men called in to the pit office, and collected three small birdcages containing canaries, small, yellow, singing birds. Then they went to the special lift, also called a cage, which would carry them deep down under the ground to where the coal lay. As soon as they stepped into the cage, the giant pit-head wheel turned, and the mechanism made the cage sink faster and further under the ground. When it arrived at the bottom of the shaft, the men walked out of the cage.

They were standing at the beginning of a long tunnel. They began to walk down the tunnel, leaving one birdcage on a special hook in the earth wall. Half-way down the tunnel they hung the second birdcage on another hook, and at the end of the tunnel, where the coal seam began, they hung the third birdcage.

Then the men began to dig. There were no machines to help them in those days. The men hacked out the coal with a pick-axe, and shovelled it up with a spade, or with their bare hands. The coal peices went into small trolleys on wheels beside the men. The mine was cold, dark, dirty, damp and dangerous.

After a few hours of hard digging, until their backs were aching and their hands sore, the men stopped to eat their lunch. There was no warm dining room for them to go to; no hot meal cooked in a kitchen. They simply sat where they were, on the cold, dark, dirty floor, to eat what they had in their boxes.

It was while they were sitting there on this particular day that one of the Jones' boys noticed the canaries in their birdcage: or rather, he didn't notice them, because he couldn't see them on their perches. He got up to have a closer look by the light on his pit helmet. All the canaries were lying on the bottom of the birdcage. The Jones' boy felt fear. He knew what that meant. Deep down under the ground where the men were working, were dangerous seeping gases. Gases that could not be seen or smelt, but that could slowly kill a man as he breathed, without him knowing it. That's why the miners always took canaries down the pit. Canaries with their tiny lungs could be poisoned by the gases before a man with his more powerful lungs could be affected.

'Quick' shouted the Jones' boy. 'No time! Gas!'

All the men leapt to their feet, leaving food and boxes exactly where they were. They ran back down the tunnel as fast as they could grabbing the other canary cages on the way. At the bottom of the main shaft, they shouted to the men at the top and jumped into the cage. The huge pit wheel turned, slowly at first, and then faster, raising the cage up faster and faster until it reached the top and the men jumped out, breathing in lungsful of clean, fresh air. Suddenly from deep below them came the shaking sound of a gas explosion. The men were safe, thanks to the canaries, and the quick action of the Jones' boy.

Those canaries, although many of them died, saved the lives of many miners. Canaries used to be taken down lots of mines in those days, but they are not used now. Complicated machines can now test for dangerous gases underground.

There are other stories of birds which have helped to save men's lies.

Pigeons flying home with tiny messages fastened to their legs have helped men.

So you see, although birds are small, they have helped man in the past.

Prayer

Dear God, thank you for all the birds in our world.
Thank you for the birds which have helped to save men's lives.
Thank you for the birds which fill the morning with their song.
Thank you for the birds which cheer us, just by being there.
Help us to repay the birds by feeding them this winter.

Amen

Hymn

'God knows me' **C&P**

The turtle
Week 4 Talking

adapted from the Kacchapa-Jātaka

When I was small, I sometimes used to go and stay at my grandma's house. It was a good house to visit, when I was small, because it had odd-shaped rooms, nooks and crannies, and three staircases. My grandma collected all sorts of things, and never liked to throw anything away, so there were always interesting things to look at. She used to have a collection of pottery plates, jugs and pots, and it was one of these that used to fascinate me. The pot was small, it had three handles to it, and had a lovely cockerel painted on the side, with some words going all the way round to the other side. When I was very small I didn't take much notice of the words, but when I was much older, and my grandma died, and the pot was given to me, I read the words carefully. They said 'Good morning! He speaks most, who has least to say!' And, you know, it's true. If you listen to people talking, you often find that the people who talk all the time, and always have something to say, are often really not saying anything helpful or important at all, but the people who spend time listening as well as talking usually say kind, helpful, well-thought-out things.

We need to learn that there are times when it is best to talk, and times when it's better to listen, or just to be quiet.

This reminds me of a king, who didn't know when to stop talking. He was a good king at heart, and wanted to rule his kingdom fairly, but was beginning to look silly in front of his people, because once he started to speak, he didn't know when to stop. The King's chief adviser wanted to help him, but was afraid of saying anything directly to him, in case he offended the King and made matters worse instead of better.

'I'll just wait', said the adviser. 'There'll be a chance to say something, tactfully, sooner or later.'

The chance came sooner, the very next day as it happened. Close to the palace grounds was a lake, on which two geese had been living for the winter. They had made friends with a turtle, who lived there all year round. They spent many a happy hour talking together in the reeds at the side of the lake, or rather one of them talked, and two of them listened, because the turtle liked nothing better than to hear the sound of his own voice, and hardly gave the geese chance to get a word in edgeways. On this particular day, the geese had told the turtle that it was time for them now to fly north for the spring.

'Oh no!' said the turtle.'You can't fly off and leave me, not now that we're such good friends, who will I have to talk to? I'll be all on my own, and it'll be so quiet without you two, what will I do?'

'You could come with us', laughed one of the geese.

'Don't be silly', said the turtle. 'I can't fly, it takes me all my time to walk.'

'We could carry you', schemed the goose.

'No, I'm far too heavy', said the turtle.

'I have a plan that will work if you can keep your mouth closed, and not talk', said the goose.

'Well, that's easy', answered the turtle. 'There's nothing to keeping my mouth closed. I can certainly do that.' The two geese looked at each other with doubt.

'Well, if you think you can do it, here's the plan. We take a stout, strong, stick in our beaks, and you clamp your jaws onto the middle, and hold on tight. That's all there is to it. We fly up into the sky, and you keep your mouth closed and hang on. Can you do it?'

'Of course I can', said the turtle, 'Let's practise.' So, the geese chose a stout, strong stick, and held an end in each beak. The turtle gripped the centre with his bony jaws. Slowly, gracefully, in unison, the geese took off, the turtle dangled between. Gently they circled the lake and carefully landed.

'It worked,' shouted the turtle, 'it worked, let's try again.' Twice more round and over the lake they went, feeling more confident each time.

'Well, I think we're ready to set off on the journey now,' said the goose, 'ready, you two?'

'Yes', they said.

Up and up they soared, higher than on the practise runs. The turtle felt excited and exhilarated.

'This is wonderful,' he thought, 'and so easy, I simply have to keep my mouth shut.'

Over the King's palace they flew, where a servant noticed the strange sight.
'Hey!' he shouted to the others. 'Come and look at this.' Other servants crowded into the courtyard to stare. 'How stupid', they all laughed, 'just look at that!'

The turtle felt angry because they had laughed at him, but he knew he must not speak.

'How ridiculous', jeered the servants, as more of them came outside to point and stare.

'Don't you . . . ' shouted the turtle as his anger bubbled over. But he never had the chance to finish what he was saying, because as soon as he opened his mouth, he loosened his grip, and fell, like a stone to the cobbled courtyard below.

The servants, courtiers, King, Queen, and adviser gathered round the broken body.

'Such a shame', said the King's adviser, seizing his opportunity, 'that some people can't stop talking, even if their life depends on it. Some people can't learn that sometimes it's better to say nothing, can they Sir?'

'No, no indeed', replied the King quietly, and for the rest of the day he remained deep in thought. From the next day everyone noticed how the King no longer talked quite so much, but sometimes stopped to listen.

We, in school must learn that there are times when it's good to talk, and other times when it's better to be quiet and to listen.

Prayer

Thank you, God, for voices and words.
Help us to use our voices well, and not to talk so much,
    that we do not listen to others.

Amen

Hymn
'The Golden Cockerel' **SSL**

It isn't fair   *Week 4   Talking*

Some people use their tongues, not to talk too much, but to grumble and complain each time they speak. I have two neighbours, one has a lovely home, a caring family, and a part-time job, but she hasn't many friends because she is always complaining. Nothing ever seems to make her happy. My other neighbour, lives alone, has no family, finds it difficult to do even simple things because she has very bad arthritis and cannot use her hands or legs properly. Yet, she always tries to be cheerful, hardly ever complains, and always sees some good in everything and everybody. She has lots of friends and seems very happy. Today's story is about a boy who complained all the time.

There was once a boy called Simon who went to work at the King's palace. His mother had gone specially to the palace to arrange for Simon to have the job. He was a good lad at heart, but was always complaining and grumbling. His usual reply to everything was, 'It isn't fair'. He grumbled around the house all day, until at last his mother decided he should go out to work and earn a living, and see what life was like in the big, wide world, and then perhaps he wouldn't complain quite so much.

On the first day in his new job, Simon was apprenticed to the palace gardener. He was given a fork and a trowel and told to dig up the weeds round the royal cabbages. At first Simon worked quite hard in the garden, and enjoyed what he was doing, until he happened to glance up and look into the royal kitchen window. He saw the chefs in their white jackets and tall chef's hats, preparing delicious dishes for the royal dinner.

'Oh – it's not fair', said Simon to himself. 'Those chefs have special uniforms to wear for their jobs. They're important and everyone recognises them in their special clothes. I want special clothes, I've only got old clothes to work in'. At the end of the day he told the gardener, who told the duty officer, who told the overseer who told the King that Simon wanted to have special clothes and be a chef. 'Very well', said the King.

The next day Simon set to work in the Royal kitchen wearing new blue check trousers, white jacket and tall chef's hat. He worked at the long wooden table and prepared the cherries for the Queen's cherry pie. At first Simon worked quite hard in the kitchen, and enjoyed what he was doing, until he happened to glance up and look through the window. He saw the royal coach being driven past by the Royal coachman. Two more coachmen in scarlet, purple and gold livery, and wearing black and gold braid tricorn hats, stood at the rear of the coach. The horses wore golden harness and tossed white plumes on their heads.

'Oh, it's not fair', cried Simon. 'Look at their beautiful coloured uniforms. Look at the gold braid and the silver tassels. It's not fair, all I've got is a white and blue uniform, I want to be a coachman and wear grand livery.' He went to tell chef, who told the duty officer, who told the overseer, who told the King that Simon thought it wasn't fair, and now he wanted to be a coachman. 'Very well', said the King.

The next day Simon set to work in the Royal stables. He wore a leather apron and his scarlet and gold livery hung on a hook by the door, and he brushed the horses' coats until they shone. At first Simon worked quite hard in the stable and enjoyed what he was doing, until he rode at the back of the coach in his new livery, and looked in through the palace dining room window. There he saw the butler in his black waistcoat and white gloves polishing the silver knives and forks, and setting the table with gleaming, golden plates.

'Oh, it's not fair', shouted Simon. 'Look at him, working inside where it's warm and dry. I'm out here where it's cold and windy. I want to work in there, and set out that beautiful dining table for the banquet, it's not fair.' He went to tell the coachman, who told the duty officer, who told the overseer, who told the King that Simon thought it wasn't fair and now he wanted to work inside and be a butler. 'Very well', said the King.

The next day Simon went to work in the Royal dining room. He wore a black waistcoat and white gloves and had to set the huge dining table with one hundred knives and forks and spoons, plates and bowls and glasses. He worked quite hard at first and enjoyed what he was doing, until he stood back at the edge of the room and watched the King and all his friends sit down at the enormous table and start to eat the magnificent banquet.

'Oh, it's not fair', yelled Simon. 'Look at the King. He doesn't have to do any work at all, everyone else does the work, and he does nothing. It's not fair, I want to be King!'

Silence fell on the room. No-one moved. No-one spoke. All were afraid of what the King would say. But the King was a wise man. Slowly he got up from his chair.

'I have decided to give all my workers a present', he said. 'All the people who work outdoors – the gardeners and the coachmen and the gatekeepers can have £100 each. All the people who work indoors, the cooks and chefs, the maids and butlers can have £100 each. And I shall have a present of £100 to spend as well, because I too, have my work to do.'

'But it's not fair', said Simon. 'I don't know whether I work inside or outside. I don't know what my work is. I haven't got a present.'

'That's right', answered the King. 'It's not fair because you're not fair. You haven't given any of your jobs a fair chance. If you did your best and stopped grumbling you would do better. Now, there's a job for you as my special messenger, if you want it, and if you learn to use your tongue wisely.'

'That's fair', said Simon.

Perhaps we can all try hard, especially this week, to be cheerful, and not to grumble. Perhaps instead of grumbling, we could try to do something to put right whatever we are grumbling about. It may not be possible, but we could try.

Prayer

It isn't fair God! It isn't fair that some people don't have enough to eat.
It isn't fair that some people are handicapped.
It isn't fair that some people are at war with others.
It isn't fair, that we who have so much, often grumble.
Help us to be thankful for all that we have, and
help us to do what we can for others.

Amen

Hymn
'Join with us' **C&P**

Sam Spell

There was once a boy (who was one of those boys) who, when he was good
he was very very good, but when he was bad he was horrid! The boy was
very good at lots of things in school. He was good at reading and writing,
good at number work, good at making things with his hands, and at drawing
and painting. He could swim well and was good at football. There was just
one thing he wasn't good at, and that was controlling his tongue! He used
to talk when he should have been quiet, he argued with his friends, and
sometimes he even answered back when his teacher spoke to him.

On one particular day, the boy had a bad morning. He argued with his
Mum before he even set off for school, he fell out with some of his friends
on the way to school, he was in trouble during the morning for talking when
he should have been working, and he got into an argument at playtime and
said a lot of things he later wished he hadn't said. By dinner-time he was
feeling thoroughly miserable and cross with himself and the world.

It was the boy's turn to use the computer. He should have been working
with his friend, but after the playtime argument, the friend no longer wanted
to sit with him. So the boy sat at the keyboard alone. He chose an easy
program – one that he had used before – it was a simple, word-puzzle
program, too easy really for the boy. The program's name was 'Sam Spell',
and the cartoon man with an enormous pencil gave clues, to which the
children typed in their answers. If they got the answer right, Sam Spell said,
'Well done, here's your next clue.' If they did not type in the right answer
Sam Spell said, 'Wrong. Try again.' The boy started the program.*

'Five fingers on it, helps you write', said Sam Spell. H A N D, typed in
the boy.

'Well done,' said Sam Spell. 'Here's your next clue – Build by the seaside, build a castle out of . . . S A N D, typed in the boy.

'Well done', said Sam Spell. 'Here's your next clue – A group of people, playing music is a . . . B A N D, typed in the boy.

'This is too easy for me,' sighed the boy, reaching out his hand to escape from the program. 'This is boring.'

As the boy's finger stretched to the key, Sam Spell grew on the screen, his finger pointing to the boy.

'Don't you dare turn me off', commanded Sam Spell. The boy stared at the screen. 'You can't speak to me like that', he declared. 'You're not programmed to have a real conversation with me. You're only programmed to play this word game.'

'I'm programmed to say anything I need to say', said Sam Spell. 'Now listen to me. Since you're bored with this game, here's a new one, listen carefully. What's a tiny piece of you that helps you speak?' M O U T H, typed in the boy. 'Wrong', said Sam Spell, 'try again!'

The boy thought. L I P S, he typed in.

'Wrong', said Sam Spell, 'try again.'

The boy thought harder. T O N G U E, he typed in.

'Well done', said Sam Spell. 'Now, what's a tiny piece of you that's hard to control?'

T O N G U E, thought the boy, puzzled, and he typed it in.

'Well done again', said Sam Spell. 'Here's the next clue. What's a tiny piece of you that can be very kind, helpful, encouraging and useful?'

T O N G U E, typed in the boy hesitantly.

'Good. Good,' enthused Sam Spell, 'and what is a tiny piece of you which can be cruel, unkind, hurtful, nasty and a nuisance?'

T O N G U E, typed the boy.

'Yes, yes, and what is a tiny piece of you that used well can make you feel very happy, but used carelessly can make you feel very unhappy?'

T O N G U E, typed the boy.

'Well done', said Sam Spell. 'Perhaps now you understand that your tongue can be your best friend or your worst enemy. Use it well.'

As the boy gazed at the screen, Sam Spell grew smaller and smaller, until he disappeared completely from view.

The boy yawned and stretched. 'I must have day-dreamed', he thought. 'I'm sure Sam Spell spoke to me.'

He ran the program through twice more, but never again did Sam Spell use the word 'tongue' in the word game. But day-dream or not, the boy remembered, and tried to use his tongue wisely from then on.

Let us, in our school try to use our tongues wisely.

Prayer

>Dear God, please help us to make our tongues into our best friends.
>Help us to use them wisely and carefully.
>Help us to make our tongues say kind and helpful things and not unkind,
>   cruel or quarrelsome things.
>
>   *Amen*

Hymn
'The ink is black' **C&P**

*I used the hall blackboard (a pinned-up sheet of paper and felt pen would substitute) and chalk to plot in game and draw 'Sam Spell'. In the early part of the story the children were able to participate and guess answers, as the boy in the story did. Thus they were actively involved in the story itself.

Sam Spell

The sorcerer's apprentice   *Week 5   Listening*
adapted from Goethe

We are all very lucky because we can hear, but not everyone can. Some people are deaf or partially hearing, that means they can't hear at all, or they can only partly hear – they can't hear properly. Those people are not able to hear all the sounds that we enjoy. Think of all the things you hear in a day. You hear your mum or dad calling you to get up, you hear the sounds of your breakfast being got ready. You hear traffic noises, birds singing, your friends, the school bell; then you hear your teacher's voices. You hear the radio, television, people talking to you, music. You know what to do because you hear people telling you. You learn a lot by using your ears. Think what it would be like if you couldn't hear.

Sometimes, though, even though you can hear, you don't always listen. Sometimes you don't listen carefully to what you are being told to do.

Today's story is about a boy who could hear; but he was lazy, and didn't listen properly. The boy lived a long time ago, in a faraway land. He was apprenticed to a powerful wizard, or sorcerer. The boy worked for the sorcerer, did jobs for him, and the sorcerer taught the boy some of his magic secrets. The sorcerer made most of his spells in a big, black cauldron, full of water. The magic ingredients were added to the water, and the sorcerer stirred the liquid, and muttered magic words. The spells needed lots of water, and it was the boy's job to carry buckets of water from the river, back to the cauldron in the cellar. The work was hard and the boy hated the job. He was not a good apprentice, he never listened and so when he was allowed to make magic spells, they always went wrong.

One day the sorcerer called to the boy to fetch more water. The boy heard, but he took no notice. 'Let him get it himself', he said, 'I'm staying here', and he lay on the grass near the cellar window, watching the sorcerer at his work.

But the sorcerer did not get the water himself. When the boy didn't come, the sorcerer muttered magic murmurs to the broomstick propped in the corner of the cellar. Instantly, the broomstick sprang alive. It sprouted arms and legs, did a somersault, and its twiggy brush became its head. The boy gaped in astonishment. The broomstick grabbed two buckets, leapt with a spring into the river, and in a trice was back with the buckets filled. The sorcerer poured the water into the cauldron, muttered more magic words, and the broom went back to its corner, and back to normal. The boy, in his hiding place in the grass, could hardly believe his eyes.

A few days later, the sorcerer had to go away on business. He left instructions for the boy to keep the cauldron filled with water, and to stir it every half hour. The boy looked into the nearly empty cauldron, and thought of all the buckets of water he would have to carry to fill it. Then he had an idea.

'Why should I carry water, when I can have that old broomstick do it for me?' he said to himself. 'I think I can remember the words the sorcerer used to bring alive the broomstick.' He walked to the stick in the corner and said the words he thought the sorcerer had used. The broomstick once more sprang to life. His wooden arms grabbed two buckets, and its wooden legs rushed it away to the river and back, with water splashing and spilling from the buckets. The broomstick poured the water into the cauldron and hurried away for more. In no time it was back, water tipping from its buckets on the way. Into the cauldron went the rest of the water, and on again to the river went the broomstick. Backwards and forwards it went, faster and faster, dripping puddles of water everywhere. The cellar floor was now awash, but the boy didn't care, the cauldron was nearly full, and he hadn't had to do any of the work. Two more bucketsful and the cauldron would be filled. Into the cellar came the last two buckets.

'Hurray!' shouted the boy. 'That's enough now. Stop. Back to your corner!' But the broomstick took no notice. On again to the river it went, back with the water into the cauldron. The water poured from the cauldron and cascaded to the floor. Back went the broomstick for more, faster, still faster.

'Stop!' shrieked the boy, but it was no use, he had not listened for the words that would stop the magic. Soon the water was waist-high, and up to the cellar window sill. The boy was frantic. He grabbed an axe and tried to chop the broomstick down, the stick dodged and weaved, the boy chopped again – and cut the broomstick clean in half. 'There', he sighed with relief. But no sooner had the sigh escaped his lips than the two halves of the broomstick each grew arms, legs and a head, and now two sticks with four buckets ran to the river and back. Water began to pour down the street. It ran down the path and reached the feet of the sorcerer walking up the path.

The sorcerer grumbled into his beard and waved his arms towards the cellar. There was a huge flash, and a crash and a whoosh of silver smoke.

When the smoke cleared the last drops of water were emptying out of the cellar and running away to the river. The broom was whole again in its corner. Only the boy showed signs of what had happened. He was pale, afraid, trembling, and dripping from head to foot.

'You had better get dry', said the sorcerer.

He never said anything more about that awful day, but from then on the boy listened carefully to everything that was said to him.

We don't have to help with magic spells, like the boy in the story, but we do help with jobs at school and at home. Let's make sure that we listen properly to what we're supposed to do, then hopefully we won't have disasters like the sorcerer's apprentice.

Prayer

Dear God, thank you for the gift of hearing.
Help us to use our ears well.
Help us to listen carefully when we are asked to do something
at home or at school.

Amen

Hymn
'Hands to work and feet to run' **SSL**

Jonah and the whale
adapted from the Bible

Week 5   Listening

We heard in our last assembly of a boy who didn't listen properly. Today I have a story about a man who didn't listen to what God told him to do. The man was given instructions by God, to do a certain job, but he didn't do as he was told – not until the end of the story, that is; but by then he had learned his lesson.

The man's name was Jonah. One day God spoke to Jonah and told him to go to a city called Nineveh and tell the people there to live good and honest lives, and to believe in God. But Jonah was afraid to go, for Nineveh was a wicked city full of dishonesty and crime. Nineveh was also quite a distance away in a country called Assyria, and the Assyrians were enemies of Jonah's people, the Israelites.

'What good can I do, if I go there?' thought Jonah. 'They won't take any notice of me. They will think I am their enemy, and they will kill me. I won't go. I'll run away, a long way from here, where God can't find me.' Jonah forgot that God is everywhere and knows everything.

So Jonah ran away, to a place called Joppa, by the sea. There was a ship just about to set sail.

'Where are you sailing to?' Jonah asked the sea captain.

'Far away west', said the man.

'Can I come with you?' asked Jonah. 'I'll pay my fare!'

'Why do you want to come?' asked the captain.

'I'm running away from God', answered Jonah.

'Well you can come', said the captain, but all the sailors laughed at Jonah, for they knew that he couldn't run away from God, because God is everywhere.

Jonah went down to the bottom of the ship and hid there. He didn't come up on deck to watch as the ship set sail. He didn't come up to watch the land slipping away, or to see the great expanse of ocean. He curled up in a dark corner at the bottom of the ship, and tried to go to sleep.

But Jonah could not sleep, because no sooner had the ship set sail, than a great storm arose. The wind roared, the rain beat down,* and monstrous waves rushed down on the small ship and it was tossed about on the foam like a tiny matchbox.

The sailors were very afraid. 'Why is this happening to us?' they asked. 'We never usually have storms like this, in this part of the ocean.'

'Perhaps Jonah's God is angry with him for running away', said one of the sailors. 'Perhaps he has sent the storm to show Jonah he is angry.'

The men went below to speak to Jonah, and to tell him what they thought.

'It must be true,' said Jonah, 'but it is not fair that you should suffer as well, it is not your fault, you have not run away. This is all my fault. Throw me into the sea and then I will drown, but you will all be safe. The storm will pass if you throw me into the sea.'

'No!' cried the men. 'We will row back to land and then you can get off our ship, and we will set off again without you.'

But, try as they might, the men could not row back to land, the storm was too fierce for them. At last they agreed that the only thing they could do, was to throw Jonah into the waves. They picked him up and threw him overboard. Straightaway the wind died down, the rain stopped, and the waves grew calm again. The ship sailed on.

Jonah sank down beneath the waves, gasping for air, and knowing that soon he would die.

But Jonah didn't die. The strangest thing happened. An enormous whale swam by, and swallowed Jonah whole! For three days and three nights Jonah lived in the stomach of the whale. He was desperately afraid and thought that being dead would be better than this.

After three days, the whale swam to a beach, and coughed up Jonah on to the sand. Jonah sat there looking startled. As he sat there, God spoke to Jonah again. 'Now will you go to Nineveh, and tell the people there to live good and honest lives and to believe in me?' he said.

'Yes', said Jonah, 'I will.'

And that is exactly what Jonah did. The people of Nineveh did not kill him, but began to lead better lives when Jonah had spoken to them.

It is a pity that Jonah needed telling twice to do what God wanted. Perhaps if he had done as he was asked straight away, he wouldn't have had that frightening time in the sea. We must try hard to do what we are asked to do, the first time we are asked, so that we don't have to be asked twice.

Prayer

Help us, God, to listen when you speak to us.

Help us to hear the voice of our conscience when it speaks.

Help us to listen to the inner voice that tells us right from wrong.

Amen

Hymn
'Who put the colours in the rainbow' **C&P**

*At this point, in the telling of the story, a terrific rainstorm began, complete with howling wind and beating rain. The noise in the assembly hall was quite fearful, even the staff felt anxious for the security of the building. The children however, were transfixed! Never in the history of our school assemblies have weather conditions been so well timed. The worst of the storm died away as the whale delivered Jonah to the land!

Unfortunately, I can offer no suggestions for the re-creation of these magical sound and lighting effects in the re-telling of future stories!

The miller, his son and the donkey
adapted from Aesop

Week 5   Listening

This week we have been thinking about listening carefully to what we are told. Quite often we need to listen not only to what other people are telling us, but to the voice of our conscience. We all have a conscience; a tiny voice inside our head that tells us what is right and what is wrong. The secret is to take notice of our conscience and to do what *it* tells us.*

Today's story is about a miller who was very good at doing what other people told him, but no good at all at using his common sense and listening to his conscience.

One day the miller and his son set off for market to sell their donkey. The day was sunny, the road clear, the man and his boy felt cheerful and happy. They walked along beside the donkey, talking together.

They had not gone far when they met a group of girls, laughing and giggling by the roadside.

'Just look at those stupid people', said one, 'walking, when one of them could be riding on the donkey. Get up and ride, one of you!'

The miller, the boy and the donkey stopped; and the man helped his son up on to the back of the donkey. Feeling well pleased with themselves, they set off again, towards the market.

A little further down the road, they passed a group of old men, sitting on a seat at the roadside, talking over the problems of the world.

'You see what I mean', said one of the old men, pointing to the miller, and his boy riding on the donkey. 'Young people have no respect for older people these days. Just look at that boy riding, while his poor father has to walk. Get down lad, and let the old man ride. Your legs are young enough to walk.'

The miller, the boy and the donkey stopped. The man helped his son down from the donkey, and the son helped his father up on to the donkey's back. Feeling well pleased with themselves, they set off again towards the market.

A little further still along the road, they met a group of women, carrying their babies and small children in their arms.

'Well, would you believe your eyes?' said one of the women. 'Would you just look at that? There's a selfish man if ever I saw one; riding up there in style like a king on a carriage, whilst that poor little boy can hardly keep up. Shame on you man,' she shouted. 'Take the boy on the donkey's back with you; the poor little lad.'

The miller, the boy and the donkey stopped. The man leaned down and helped his son up behind him on the donkey's back.

Feeling well pleased with themselves, they set off again towards the market.

Soon they came to the bridge over the river. Over the other side of the bridge they could see the brightly coloured market stalls, the tradespeople selling their wares from tables and baskets and pathways; and crowds, pushing and jostling to get a better look at everything on sale. They hurried over the bridge. Coming towards them was a shepherd and his sheep.

'Is that your donkey?' asked the shepherd.

'Yes', said the miller.

'Then I don't think you're treating him very well', said the shepherd. 'He'll be worn out by the time you get him to market, carrying you two. Poor animal, you'd do better to carry him, instead of him carrying you', and the shepherd took his sheep over the bridge.

The miller, the boy and the donkey stopped. The miller by now was very good at doing what he was told, so without further ado, he and the boy hoisted the donkey onto their shoulders and walked into the market place.

The people stood and stared, then laughed, pointed and sniggered, at the foolish two, shouldering a donkey between them.

'Have you ever seen anything so silly', they jeered, 'as a grown man and a boy carrying a donkey?'

At the sound of all the fuss and commotion, the poor donkey, almost frightened out of his wits, struggled and kicked to free himself. He butted the miller and kicked the son, clattered down on to the cobble stones, splashed through the river, and galloped away as fast as his legs would carry him, never to be seen again.

The miller and his son stood in the market place, looking foolish, surrounded by laughing crowds. Slowly and in silence they turned and walked back home.

'In future,' said the miller, 'I shall do what I think is right, never mind what people say.'

The miller learned his lesson, and tried from then on to listen to the voice of his conscience, and to do what he knew to be right. When our friends tell us to do something, we must decide for ourselves if it is right or not. If we think it is right, that's fine, we go ahead and do it; if we think it is wrong, we firmly say 'No'.

Prayer

Dear God, when people tell us to do things,
help us to think for ourselves and use our consciences to guide us.
Help us to remember that people who care for us,
like our parents and our teachers, will not tell us to do things
that will hurt us,
but if strangers or even our friends tell us to do things,
we must do what we know to be right.

Amen

Hymn

'One more step' **C&P**

*At this point I asked the children to see how good they were at listening. In a very quiet voice I gave them various instructions, eg. put your hands on your heads, stand up, turn to face your neighbour etc. (with good control, this was done in total silence and no fuss). When all were again seated and still, I asked what they would do if I told them to roll in the mud or jump through a window. Many hands went up to tell me they would not do it. 'Why?' 'Because we're not to and it's dangerous.' I praised this reply and stressed that parents and teachers will not tell them to do anything dangerous or silly, but that it was good that they used their own brains and listened to their own consciences. This they must do all the time, especially when friends or strangers tell them to do something. 'Because Tommy told me to', is no excuse for getting into trouble.

Picasso and Bob Geldof

Week 6   *Famous people*

Not long ago, lived a very famous painter called Picasso. Picasso painted pictures, lots of pictures, during his lifetime. Some people liked his pictures and said, 'Picasso is one of the greatest painters who ever lived. Picasso's paintings are different, original, unique. Picasso's paintings are wonderful.' Other people looked at Picasso's paintings, many of which were more like patterns than pictures, and they said 'What rubbish! He can't paint for toffee. Look at the paintings, they don't even look like what they're supposed to be. Any fool can paint pictures like that!' But those people were wrong. For what they didn't know was that before Picasso began to paint his pictures-like-patterns, he learnt how to paint 'properly'. He learned about paint and canvases and brushes. He learned about light and shade, and how to paint so that the things he painted looked real enough to touch.* In the beginning, when he first began to paint, he painted pictures that looked as real as photographs. Then he began to feel dissatisfied, he wanted to paint pictures that were different, pictures that were his, pictures that people would look at and say 'Picasso painted that', without even looking at his name in the corner. So Picasso began to experiment with colours and shapes, and he began to paint his pattern-pictures. He developed his own way of painting, but only after he had learned to paint 'properly'.

I can think of a pop star – you will have probably seen him on television. He has become very famous because of the help he has given the people of Africa. Some people think he is outspoken, and others say he is scruffy and untidy, but whatever people think of him, he has worked hard and done his best to help the African people.

He decided when he was quite young that he wanted to be a pop star, so he worked hard, formed a group, practised and practised, and made some records. He became well known as a pop star. One day he heard about the millions of people who were dying of starvation in Africa and he decided he wanted to help. He decided to invite all his pop star friends to help as well. He decided to work his hardest and do his best to raise money to help the starving people of Africa.

He organised all his pop star friends into a huge group which he called Band Aid and they made a record. The money the record made was given to the African people for food. He then organised Live Aid, the biggest pop festival the world had ever seen. The money raised from that also went to help the starving people. The pop star helped to raise £58 million for famine relief.

Who is he?

Yes. Bob Geldof.

We can't all be famous painters like Picasso or famous pop stars like Bob Geldof, but we can all learn how to do things properly and learn how to do our best like those two people. Remember, they learned how to do things properly before they developed their own style, and they did their best all the time, whatever they were doing.

Prayer

Dear God, help us to remember that if a thing is worth doing,
   it is worth doing well.
Help us to do everything we do, properly and well.
Help us to do our best all the time.

Amen

Hymn
'The best gift' **C&P**

*I showed the children reproductions of Picasso's work. I chose 'Portrait of a Painter after El Greco' (1950) and 'First Steps' (1943) as examples of his later work, and 'The Altar Boy' (1896) and 'Portrait of Gertrude Stein' (1906), as examples of his earlier style. Other paintings could also be shown to illustrate Picasso's early and later style.

Hans Andersen
Week 6   Famous people

If I were to ask you which is your favourite story, I wonder which one you would choose. I have lots of favourites, and one of the stories I like best of all is called 'Great Claus and Little Claus'. It is a story about two men who were both called Claus. One had four horses, so he was called Great Claus, and the other had just one horse, so he was called Little Claus. Quite a lot of you know the story because I have read it to you. All stories of course are written by someone, and that story was written by a famous writer called Hans Andersen. He wrote many stories, but he wasn't always famous.

Hans Andersen was born in Denmark nearly two hundred years ago. When he was a boy Hans lived in his father's shoemakers shop, and he was supposed to go to school to learn to read and write and do sums. His father wanted Hans to work hard at school and then to learn to become a shoemaker like him, so they could work together. But Hans did not work hard at school, in fact he didn't go to school very often, and his father was usually too busy to make him go. Hans used to stay at home and play with his toy theatre. He didn't want to be a shoemaker when he grew up, but decided he wanted to be a famous opera singer instead.

Sometimes, when the other children had finished school for the day, they would go round to Hans' house and ask him to tell them a story, because he was very good at making up stories and telling them. He made up stories about a tin soldier, an ugly duckling, a ballerina, some red shoes, and lots more things.

One day when Hans was fourteen, he left home and walked to the town of Copenhagen. 'I am going to be a famous opera singer', he said. He went to the big theatre in Copenhagen, and walked inside, and onto the stage.

'I want to be a famous opera singer', he said to the people there, but they simply laughed at him and told him to go away. Hans went back to the theatre every day, and every day he told the people there that he wanted to be a famous opera singer. Every day, the people laughed and told him to go away, until one day someone said, 'Well, if you want to be a singer, sing! Let us hear what you sound like.'

So Hans stood in the middle of the stage and sang. The noise was dreadful! He couldn't sing in tune at all, and he couldn't remember the words. 'You can't sing', the people said. 'You can't sing at all, so you can't be an opera singer', and they all laughed at him again. One lady in the opera company felt sorry for Hans and she said, 'You are not very good at singing, but you must be good at something. What are you good at?'

Everyone listened and waited to hear what Hans would say. What could he say? He wasn't any good at anything. Then he remembered the stories he used to tell the children at home.

'I can tell good stories', he said, and standing there in the middle of the stage he told them a wonderful story about a rich emperor who wanted some new clothes. The people listened, entranced. The story was exciting, and amusing, it made them laugh and it made them think. When Hans finished the story, the people burst into cheering and clapping.

'That was good', they all said. 'You should write it down, and become a writer instead of an opera singer.'

'That's a good idea,' said the lady. 'Write your story down and I'll show it to the King, he'll like it.'

So Hans wrote his story down, but now he wished he had tried harder with his reading and writing at school. He found it very easy to tell the story, but he found it very hard to write it down. At last it was finished, and the lady took the story to show the King.

'Hmm!' said the King. 'It's a very good story, but Hans isn't very good at writing and spelling, is he? He should go to school again and learn how to write and spell properly. Send him to school, and send me the bill, I'll pay.'

Hans went back to school again to try harder with his reading, writing and spelling. He worked well, and soon was as good at writing stories as telling them. He wrote another story for the King, and this time the King said, 'Yes! It's good. Write me another and another and another.'

Soon Hans Andersen's stories were made into books and he became a famous writer.

Prayer
> Dear God, thank you for writers who have written stories
> > for us to read and enjoy.
> Help us to work hard at our reading and writing,
> > so that we can read stories that other people have written,
> > and write stories of our own.
> > > > > > > > > > > *Amen*

Hymn
'The ink is black' **C&P**

The robot project

This week we have been thinking about famous people. There are many, many famous people in the world, but most of them have something in common. Most of them are famous because they did something original; they did something their own way, properly, but in their own way, using their own ideas and imagination. They didn't copy what someone else was doing. Picasso, when he had learned how to paint, developed his own style, painted his pictures his way, he didn't copy another painter's style. Hans Andersen, when he had learned to read and write properly, wrote his own, imaginative stories. He did not copy other people's ideas, but used his own.

We need to be like those people. When we paint a picture, or write a story, we need to do our own work, not copy what our next-door-neighbour is doing, or make ours the same as our friends'. When your teacher asks you to write a story, she doesn't want to read 30 stories, all more or less alike, she wants to read 30 completely different stories, because they have been written by quite different people.

There was once a class of children which had been doing a project about robots. The children had collected books and information about robots; they had pretended to be robots in dance and music; they had even made a larger-than-life model robot in the corner of their classroom, complete with flashing lights, and a synthesised voice which could be turned off and on by hidden switches. Their teacher asked them one day, to do part of the project at home, and it was to be a competition. They were to design an 'automatic rubbish disposal unit' which could be attached to their classroom robot, and which could then get rid of all their daily classroom rubbish; sweet papers, apple cores, waste paper, milk bottle tops, straws, bits of old Plasticine; everything. They were to draw a picture of their invention, and then at school the next day they were to write about their invention, and explain how it worked.

The teacher had found the idea for this in a book for teachers, about creative writing, and the book had in it writing and a picture that a child in the author's school had made.

That afternoon all the children in that class went home full of ideas for their picture; all that is, except one girl. Her mum had been a teacher, and the girl knew that at home there was a book, with a picture of a robot, and an automatic rubbish disposal unit, in it. She also knew that the picture had a piece of writing to go with it, and that both the picture and the writing had been made up by a child of about her age.

'All I need to do, is copy it,' said the girl. 'It's bound to win the competition, because it's so good. It must be good if it's in a book.'

That evening after tea, when all the rest of the children in her class were making up their own pictures for the competition, the girl carefully copied the picture out of the book, and carefully read the piece of writing that went with it so that she could write the same the next day at school.

The next day arrived and all the children were looking at each others' drawings of the invention.

'Yours is good', lots of people said to the girl, 'I bet yours wins!'

Later that morning the teacher asked all the children to write about their invention, and then the drawing and the writing could be judged in the competition.

Everyone tried their hardest. The girl tried to remember exactly what the writing in the book had been, so that her writing could be the same.

Soon, everyone had finished, and the teacher collected all the drawings and pieces of writing together.

Later that afternoon, the teacher announced the winner. It was the girl. Everyone clapped and said well done, and said she deserved to win because her drawing had been so good. But the girl did not feel happy. Deep inside her she felt awful. She knew it was wrong for her to be the winner, because the work was not her own.

At home time she was last out of the classroom. Just she and her teacher were there. The teacher said, 'Have you anything to tell me, Julie?' The girl looked at the teacher and started to cry. Then she told her story, and said, 'But why did you let me win when you knew I had cheated?'

'Because I wanted you to choose for yourself the right or the wrong thing to do', said the teacher.

'I'm sorry', said Julie.

'Yes, I know you are,' said Mrs Briggs, 'tomorrow we'll tell the children there was a mistake, and I'll announce the real winner.'

Julie never tried to cheat again, she always did her own work, and never copied from anyone again to pretend the work was her own.

If you always do your own work, as well as you are able, everyone will always say that you have done your best.

Prayer
> Dear God, help me always to do my best.
> Help me to know that I am me; with ideas, imagination
> and a conscience of my own.
> Help me to put my ideas, my imagination
> and my conscience to good use.

Amen

Hymn
'Kum ba yah' **C&P**

Joseph – the Favourite
adapted from the Bible

Last week we were thinking about famous people, and this week we are going to think about a famous story. This story is one of my favourites and is one of the most exciting in the Bible. The story has been made into a pop musical, and we will hear some of the music from it at the end of assembly.* You might like to make some pictures of the story, and we will put them up in the hall when they are ready.

The story started hundreds of years ago in Canaan, where Jacob lived with his twelve sons. Reuben was the oldest son, Benjamin was the youngest son, but it was Joseph, without a doubt, who was the favourite son. The other brothers were always a little jealous of Joseph, because their father liked him the best.

'I don't see why he should be the favourite one', said Benjamin. 'He should be the least favourite. He's always sitting about day-dreaming. He doesn't work as hard as the rest of us.'

It was certainly true that Joseph spent a good deal of time sitting dreaming to himself.

One day, the eleven brothers became even more jealous of Joseph, because Jacob bought him a beautiful new coat. The older brothers wore sheepskin coats to keep out the cold, but this coat for Joseph was fit for a king. It was very expensive and was made of fine cloth in every colour of the rainbow. The coat glistened and glimmered as it caught the light of the sun in the day or the moon at night. It was a splendid, magnificent coat.

'He won't be able to do *any* work now', grumbled the brothers, 'he'll be worried about getting his beautiful new coat dirty.'

A few days after he was given his new coat, Joseph got up in the morning and said to the eleven brothers, 'Listen. I had a strange dream last night. I dreamt we were making sheaves of corn in a field, and all your sheaves of corn stood round in a circle and bowed down to mine.'

The brothers were angry when they heard this and said, 'So, you think you're more important than us do you? You're only the second youngest you know. You're not the most important.'

A week later, Joseph had another dream and he told his brothers about it. 'I dreamt that I was a star,' he said, 'and the sun and moon and eleven other stars all bowed down before me.'

This time the brothers were so angry with Joseph because they thought he was being big-headed, that they decided to do something about him.

'We'll kill him', said one.

'We'll throw him into a pit and leave him to die', said another.

'But our father will be angry with us', said a third.

'Then we won't tell him the truth. We'll tell him that a wild animal has killed Joseph. He won't know it was us', said a fourth.

'I don't think we should', whispered Benjamin, but no-one heard him, so it was decided that Joseph should be killed.

The very next day, the brothers went into the fields to work and Joseph stayed at home. After a while, Jacob told Joseph to go and see what his brothers were doing, and whether they were working hard in the fields.

Joseph set off, wearing his beautiful new coat. 'Here he is,' said the brothers, 'coming to spy on us to see what we are doing. Let's do it now! Let's throw him into that pit and leave him to die.'

As soon as Joseph reached the brothers, they began to bow down and make fun of him.

'Oh, wonderful wise one', they mocked.

'We bow down and worship you', they laughed. Then they grabbed hold of him, tore off the beautiful, new coat, and threw Joseph to the bottom of a deep pit. Joseph could not escape.

The brothers were just about to leave him there to die, when they saw some men on camels, riding towards them. One of the brothers said, 'Let's sell him as a slave, then we don't have to kill him.' They pulled Joseph out of the pit with a rope, and sold him to the travelling merchants for twenty pieces of silver. The merchants rode away into the distance taking Joseph with them, still tied up with the rope.

The brothers took Joseph's beautiful new coat, dipped it in the blood of an animal, and took it home to Jacob. They told Jacob, 'Joseph has been killed by a wild animal. Look, here is his coat covered in blood.' Jacob was very sad.

None of the brothers was brave enough to tell Jacob the truth; that Joseph had been sold as a slave.

In our next assembly we will hear what happened to Joseph next.

Prayer

Thank you, God, for the exciting stories in the Bible.

Help us not to be jealous as Joseph's brothers were of him.

Amen

Hymn
'Sing a rainbow' **A**

*At the beginning and end of each section of the story of Joseph, excerpts from 'Joseph and the amazing technicolor dreamcoat' were played to the

children. I used the original studio recording available on MCA Records, catalogue number MCF 2544, and the accompanying hard-back book of lyrics, CN 3783.

Joseph – the Dreamer
adapted from the Bible

In our last assembly we heard the first part of the story of Joseph. His brothers had thrown Joseph into a pit, and then sold him as a slave to some merchants travelling to Egypt. They told Jacob, their father, that Joseph had been killed by a wild animal, and they showed Jacob the blood-covered coat, to prove their story.

Joseph was taken by the merchants to Egypt, where he was sold again, to Potiphar, the captain of the guard of Pharaoh's army. Joseph didn't enjoy being a slave, but he worked hard and always did his best. Potiphar was pleased with Joseph's hard work and he soon learned to trust Joseph. Before long, Potiphar had handed over the entire running of his house and lands to Joseph. It was an important job to do and Joseph did it well. But Potiphar's wife was jealous.

She made trouble for Joseph, and told lies about him to Potiphar. Potiphar believed the lies she told and threw Joseph into a dark dungeon under the house.

Joseph's prison was damp and smelly and always dark, because no daylight came into the underground dungeon. He was in the prison with two of Pharaoh's servants, and the three of them used to pass the time by telling each other of the dreams they'd had. Joseph tried to explain what the dreams meant. After a time they discovered that Joseph was always right when he explained the meaning of the dreams.

Joseph was kept in the prison for two years, and then something happened that changed everything. Pharaoh had a dream. In the dream seven fat cows walked out of the river Nile, followed by seven thin, sickly-looking cows. The thin cows ate all the fat cows, but stayed as thin as before.

Pharaoh was worried by the dream and called all his wise men to him, so that they could explain what the dream meant. But no-one could tell Pharaoh the meaning and all the wise men went away again. Then, one of Pharaoh's servants remembered Joseph in the dungeon.

'Send for him', ordered Pharaoh, and Joseph was brought to the palace.

Pharaoh told Joseph of his dream and Joseph told Pharaoh that it meant there were going to be seven years of plenty. Joseph said it would be a good idea to store all the spare food during the seven years of plenty because they would be followed by seven years of famine when the people would starve because no food would grow.

Pharaoh was so pleased that Joseph had been able to explain his dream, that he made him into the Viceroy of Egypt – the most important person in the land, second only to the Pharaoh himelf. Joseph was moved into a house in the palace grounds and was given everything that an important man would need. He travelled about the country, and everywhere he went, people bowed down to him because he was the Viceroy.

Seven years went by and Egypt became a rich and powerful country. Food was plentiful but Viceroy Joseph didn't allow it to be wasted. He ordered the farmers to store all the spare corn, and he went round the farms himelf to check that the stores were locked.

Then the famine came. For seven years nothing grew. People and animals in the countries around Egypt grew thin and died of starvation. But in Egypt, Viceroy Joseph opened the corn stores and shared out a little corn each day to the queues of starving people. The queues grew longer each day, as people from the other countries heard of Egypt's stores of corn.

One day Joseph looked down the queue of starving people waiting for food, and there he saw . . . his brothers, thin and in rags. The famine had reached Canaan where Joseph used to live, and now his brothers were starving and had come to Egypt to beg for food. They, of course, didn't know that Joseph was now the Viceroy who was second only to the Pharaoh.

Joseph looked at his starving brothers and remembered that they had wanted to kill him. He remembered that they had thrown him in a pit and then sold him as a slave into Egypt. He remembered that because of them he had lived as a prisoner in a dark dungeon.

Joseph wondered whether to give his brothers food, or whether to turn them away and let them starve.

What would you have felt like doing, if you had been Joseph? Perhaps you think Joseph should have forgiven his brothers, or perhaps you think he should let them starve, to get his own back. In the next part of the story, we'll see what Joseph did.

Prayer

> Dear God, thank you for the food we have to eat.
> Help us to try to be fair with people, as Joseph tried to be fair
> > to the people in Egypt.

Amen

Hymn
'When I needed a neighbour' **C&P**

Joseph – the Carer
adapted from the Bible

In our story of Joseph, we left him looking at the queue of starving people who had come to Egypt for food. There, in the queue, were his brothers, looking ragged, thin and ill. Joseph stared at them, wondering what to do.

Joseph counted his brothers, there were ten of them; Benjamin, the youngest brother, was missing. The brothers looked at Joseph with the pain of hunger in their eyes. They didn't recognise Joseph. They just saw the Viceroy of Egypt, the second most important man in the country. They had no idea it was Joseph.

When their turn in the queue came, Viceroy Joseph said in a stern voice, 'Who are you and where are you from?'

The brothers fell down on their knees and said, 'We are ten poor brothers who need food. Our youngest brother and our old father are at home in Canaan. Please give us food to take back.'

'How do I know you're telling the truth. You might be spies', answered Viceroy Joseph.

The brothers were afraid of this important man. 'We are telling you the truth', they said.

'Then bring me your youngest brother', said Joseph. 'I want to see him.'

The brothers were even more afraid. Why did this man want their brother: and what would their father say? He had already lost Joseph, he would be heart-broken if anything happened to Benjamin.

'Please sir, don't make us bring him', they pleaded.

'Yes, I want to see him', commanded Viceroy Joseph. 'One of you will stay here as my prisoner. The rest of you will be given food and will go home for your youngest brother.' Simeon was chosen to stay behind in Egypt, and the other brothers were given sacks of grain to take home with them. They paid for the food with the money they had brought with them, but secretly, Joseph made his servants put the money back in the brothers' sacks, on top of the grain.

The brothers set off for home. On the way one of them opened his sack of grain and was astonished to see the money he had paid, sitting there, on top of the corn.

'What does it mean?' they all cried. They were now even more afraid of the Egyptian Viceroy. Perhaps he was going to accuse them of stealing the corn.

When Jacob, their father, heard their story he wept bitterly. 'First Joseph was killed by an animal, now Simeon is a prisoner and you want to take Benjamin away. What is to become of us all? Take Benjamin, but if anything happens to him I shall die of a broken heart. Remember that!'

The brothers, this time with Benjamin, returned to Egypt, and queued once more outside the grain stores of Viceroy Joseph. As soon as Joseph saw his brothers he ordered his servants to prepare a banquet, and took the brothers together with Simeon, to his house for the feast. The brothers thought it very strange, that this man who had thought they were spies, and who had returned their money, was now giving them food fit for a king. Again they felt afraid.

Joseph invited the brothers to sleep in his palace that night, and the next morning they were given sacks of grain to take home with them. Just as before, they paid for the corn with the money they had brought with them, but, just as before, Joseph secretly made his servants put the money back in the brothers' sacks. This time Joseph also put a silver cup in Benjamin's sack. Then he said goodbye to the brothers, and they set off for Canaan.

No sooner were they out of sight of Joseph, than he ordered a servant to go after them and bring them back.

'You have stolen from me!' he shouted.

The brothers went down on their knees and bowed to Joseph, just as the sheaves of corn had done in Joseph's dream all those years before.

'We have done nothing wrong', they cried.

'You have stolen my silver cup', insisted Joseph. 'Guards, search them.'

The guards came forward and searched the brothers, and there, in Benjamin's sack was the cup.

'You will be my slave', shouted Joseph to Benjamin.

'Please, no', cried the brothers. 'Our father will die of grief if anything happens to Benjamin. Many years ago, we allowed our brother Joseph to be taken from us, and we are truly sorry. We cannot allow anything to happen to Benjamin. Please free him. Take one of us instead.'

When Joseph saw that his brothers were truly sorry for what they had done all those years ago, he said, 'Stand up and look at me. Do you not see who I am? I am Joseph, your brother.'

They stared at Viceroy Joseph in amazement; and then they saw it was Joseph, their brother. They were speechless.

'Go home', said Joseph 'and bring everyone back with you; my father, your children and grandchildren; your flocks of sheep, your cattle, everything. You shall all live here with me, and I will look after you.'

And so the whole of Joseph's family went to live in Egypt at the time of the famine, and Joseph looked after them all.

I'm pleased the story has a happy ending. I think everyone in the story learned to be kinder to each other because of what happened. Joseph learned not to be so big headed, and the brothers learned to be truly sorry for selling Joseph as a slave.

Prayer

   Thank you, God, for our families.
   Help us to care for the people in our families,
      as Joseph did at the end of the story.
   Help us to be brave enough to say we are sorry
      if we have done something wrong.

Amen

Hymn
'The family of man' **C&P**

James' and Sarah's new schools   Week 8   Friends

Once upon a time, the Rothwell family, Mr and Mrs Rothwell, James and
Sarah, had to move house. Mr Rothwell came home one evening and told
Mrs Rothwell that his firm wanted him to move to another city, quite some
way from where they lived. The job meant better money and a bigger house,
and Mrs Rothwell thought it would be better for the whole family if they
moved. James, who was ten at the time, and Sarah, who was seven, were
not happy about moving away. They had their school and their friends, and
they didn't want to leave.

'You'll soon make friends at the new house', said Mr and Mrs Rothwell.

The day of the move came. The children left their old school and said
goodbye to their friends and teachers. The furniture and boxes were packed
into the removal van, and it set off to the new house. Mr and Mrs Rothwell,
James and Sarah set off in the car.

They all spent the whole of the weekend unpacking the boxes, putting up
curtains and arranging the furniture in their new house. On Monday the
children were to start their new schools. For the first time, they were to go
to different schools. James was to go to South Park Middle School, and
Sarah was to go to Oakdene Primary School. They both felt rather nervous
on Monday morning as they set off with their mum to the new schools. They
wondered what the schools would be like.

They wondered what the teachers would be like; what the classrooms,
lessons and books would be like; what the children would be like.

James' school day started off well. The headteacher took him to his class
teacher, who sat him next to a helpful boy, and asked the boy to look after
him. During the morning all the children in James' class were friendly and
helpful. They showed him where things were kept and how they did things
at their school. They showed him where to put his English book for marking
and how to put the library books away. At playtime some boys invited James

to join in their football game, and showed him where to line up at in-time.

At lunchtime two children showed James how to line up with his tray, and where to get his food from. It was very different from his last school where everyone sat round tables of eight, but these children were helpful to James and he soon felt quite used to this new way.

At hometime that afternoon, he told his mum what a good time he'd had and how much he liked his new school. 'I've made loads of friends', he said.

Sarah did not have quite such a good day as James. She, too, was taken by the headteacher to meet her class teacher, who found Sarah a place. The teacher didn't ask anyone to look after Sarah, and no-one seemed to take much notice of her. No-one showed her what to do, or helped her to put her things away in the right place at the end of the lesson. At playtime all the children seemed to have their own friends to play with, no-one asked Sarah to play, and she was too shy to ask if she could join in. When the bell rang for in-time Sarah watched the others to see what they did, then she did the same.

At lunchtime she sat next to a girl who started talking to her, and Sarah began to tell the girl about moving house, but then a teacher asked everyone to stop talking because there was too much noise. After lunch the other girl went off to play with her friends and Sarah walked about in the playground on her own.

During the afternoon Sarah's class had P.E. and she watched the other children again to see where they put their clothes, and where they waited in the hall. It wasn't that the other children were being deliberately unfriendly, it was just that they didn't think of being helpful.

At hometime, Sarah told her mum about her day. She hadn't enjoyed it very much, and she wasn't looking forward to going again the next day.

I'm pleased to be able to tell you that Sarah did eventually settle in to her new school, and she did make friends, but it took quite a long time.

James had a much better first day than Sarah, didn't he? Why do you think he enjoyed his day more than Sarah enjoyed hers?

(Answer should mention difference in attitude and behaviour of children at the two schools).

Yes; the children at South Park School were much friendlier and more helpful than those at Oakdene.

Which of those schools do you think ours is like? (*Hopefully children will answer South Park!*)

Let's make sure we are always friendly and helpful towards any new children who come to our school.

Prayer

Thank you, God, for all my friends.
Help me to *be* a good friend.
Help me to be friendly and kind to new people in our school.
Help me to help anyone who seems to need a friend.

Amen

Hymn

'Can you count the stars?' **SSL**

Granville joins the Cubs
Week 8   Friends

In our last assembly story, two children started at new schools, and had to begin all over again to make friends. They had left all their old friends behind when they had to move house, and when they started at their new schools they didn't know anyone. One of the children, James, settled in very quickly and was happy in his new school straight away, because the children in that school were kind, and helped him to settle in. Sarah wasn't so happy at first, because no-one bothered to be friendly to her, no-one tried to help her. She did find some friends in the end but it took her a long time.

Some people seem to make friends very quickly, but other people are shy and timid and they don't make friends easily at first. To make a friend you need to show that you will *be* a friend, and often you have to be brave and be the first one to speak.

There was once a boy called Granville, who was eight. One day he was watching Blue Peter on television, and saw some cub Scouts who had won a special award. The Cubs, Granville learned, met every week after school, and took part in all kinds of games and activities; they even went on camping holidays in the summer.

'Mum', said Granville, 'can I be a Cub?'

'I think that would be a good idea', said his mum, 'but I don't know where there's a Cub pack near here. I'll ask at the library where the nearest pack is, and we'll see if you can join it.'

Granville's mum found that there was a Cub pack that met on a Thursday evening, in the church hall, not too far away from Granville's house. 'I'll ring up the Cub leader and see if they can take you', said Granville's mum.

'I suppose it will depend on whether they've a place. They may have a waiting list, and you might have to wait until they have a spare place, so don't be too disappointed if you can't start straight away', she added.

Granville's mum telephoned and was pleased to be told that Granville could start Cubs the following Thursday. All they had to do was just arrive and introduce themselves, then Granville's mum could go home and collect him later in the evening.

Granville was really looking forward to starting Cubs, but as Thursday evening came closer, he began to feel rather nervous. 'I won't know anyone, mum', he said. 'None of my friends go to Cubs, and the boys there will already have their own friends. They might not want to be friends with me.'

'I'm sure they will', answered his mum, 'but you'll have to be friendly to the boys. You just talk to them, and show them that you're friendly; not bossy, or big-headed, just friendly, then I think you'll find that someone will be friendly to you. It'll be no good just standing about waiting for them to talk to you, you have to be ready to show friendliness first.'

'Mmm,' said Granville, 'I suppose so.'

Thursday came, and Granville's mum went with him into the hall. There was a lot of noise, and a lot of boys rushing about playing a game. The Cub leader – Akela – emerged from the middle of the boys and greeted Granville and his mum.

'He'll be all right with us, you can collect him at 7.30', she said.

So Granville's mum left, and he was on his own. Some of the boys were standing around, talking now, the others were still noisily busy doing something in the middle of the floor.

'You'll soon get used to us', said Akela, and she hurried away to deal with the boys in the centre of the hall.

Granville felt very lonely. There wasn't a face he recognised, there was no-one he knew. He noticed lots of the boys looking at him, and watching him because he was new. Then he remembered what his mum had said about showing he was friendly. He gathered his courage and went over to the nearest group of boys.

'Hello'' he said, 'what was that game you were playing? I don't know that one. Will you show me how to play it?'

'Sure', said one of the Cubs. 'Look, this is what happens', and they explained the game to Granville. For the rest of the evening he joined in with everything, it was all new, but the boys were friendly and Granville showed he wanted to learn and wanted to be one of them.

When his mum called for him at 7.30, some of the other boys called to Granville, 'Goodbye. See you next week.'

'Well?' said Granville's mum on the way home.

'Great', said Granville, 'I can't wait 'til next Thursday.'

Granville quickly made lots of friends at Cubs, and knew that his mum had been right when she told him that in order to have a friend he had first to show that he was prepared to be one.

We need to remember that when we join a new class, or join a club, or begin anything with new people.

Prayer

Dear God, help us to know that to have a friend,
we must be prepared to be a friend.

Amen

Hymn
'Join with us' **C&P**

Different kinds of friends

Week 8   Friends

This week we have been thinking about our friends, and today I thought I would tell you about my friends. I have lots of different kinds of friends, and I think you will recognise some of your kinds of friends amongst these.

I have friends I see every day at school. All the teachers here are friends. We talk to each other and listen to each other each day. Sometimes we talk about our families and homes. Most of the time we talk about school, and you!

I have other friends that I don't see every day, but just see sometimes.

I have friends that are teachers in other schools. I have a friend that I used to go to school with. Sometimes we meet in the holidays and go shopping and have lunch together.

I have friends that live very near my house. They are my neighbours. Sometimes we talk when we are in our gardens. Sometimes I go to their house, and sometimes they come to mine.

Then I have a friend who likes to do the same things that I like to do. Sometimes in the holiday we have a day at the seaside, or we might go to the theatre or go to see a film.

I have some friends that I don't suppose I shall ever see again. People I have met on holiday, that have been my friends for just the two weeks of the holiday. I expect you have had holiday friends like that. Sometimes it's good to write to those holiday friends.

I have one other friend that I would like to tell you about. I know lots of things about her. She is called Marie-Claude, and she lives in France in a town called Chinon. Chinon has a castle and a river, and on Sundays, Marie-Claude likes to go with her husband and her son, Laurent, who's ten, to the park by the river. Marie-Claude's parents live quite nearby, also in Chinon. Marie-Claude is a secretary, and she works for the same company that her husband works for; it is a computer company. In her spare time, Marie-Claude likes cooking and reading, but she doesn't like sewing. Laurent goes to school each day like you, but he has different school times from you. He goes to school at eight o'clock in the morning and he comes home at one o'clock, at the beginning of the afternoon. He doesn't have his lunch at school like you, and he doesn't go back to school in the afternoon. He is learning English at school, and he likes collecting stamps and postcards.

I have known Marie-Claude now for twenty five years . . . and yet I have never met her! I know what she looks like, and yet I have never seen her. I have never been to her house and she has never been to mine!

How can she have been my friend for all that time, when we have never met each other?

(*Children answer: write letters, pen-pal, pen-friend etc*)

Yes, she is my pen-friend. She is a friend that I know by the letters she writes. Every time the postman brings a letter from her, it is just like having her talk to me. Perhaps one day we will meet each other.*

And so there are lots of different kinds of friends. Some of them we see often, some not very often, some we don't see at all. Those children in our assembly story at the beginning of the week, who had to move house and change schools, could have kept in touch with their old friends by writing letters. Writing letters to friends can be fun, and getting letters from friends is always exciting.

Friends don't have to be people who live very near. People who live a long way away can still be friends if we take the trouble to keep in touch, and keep the friendship alive.

Prayer

Dear God, thank you for our friends at home and at school.
Thank you for our friends who live a long way away.
Thank you for friends that we share things with.
Thank you for friends that we meet on holiday.
Help us to remember that everyone is a friend of someone,
      and someone is our friend.
If we remember that, it should be possible for the whole world
      to be friends.

Amen

Hymn
'The family of man' **C&P**

This assembly can obviously be adapted to suit the person taking it. However, if preferred, it can be used as it is, but put into the third person.

David's families

Everyone here belongs to a family. Lots of you have brothers and sisters, and you all have a mum or a dad or both. I expect you have grandmas and grandpas, aunts and uncles and cousins as well.

But not everyone is as lucky as you; some people don't have any family of their own, at all. Some children don't have any family of their own, they are usually looked after in children's homes.

There was once a boy called David, who didn't have a mum or dad, or a brother or a sister. He lived in a children's home, and was looked after by a lady called Auntie Barbara. She wasn't his real auntie, but she looked after all twelve boys and girls in the home, and they all called her Auntie Barbara.

One day David went to her and said, 'I haven't got a family, have I?'

'Well no,' she answered, 'you haven't a mum or dad, or brothers and sisters of your own, but you belong to a family. You belong to our family, here in this house.'

'Mmm', said David.

Later that day, David spoke to Mrs Brown, his teacher. 'I haven't got a family, have I?' he said.

'Well no, not exactly,' said Mrs Brown, 'but you do belong to our class, and we are like a family. We see each other every day, and we do things together like a family does.'

'Mmm', said David.

At playtime, David met his headteacher, Mrs Johnson, in the cloakroom.

'Hello David', she said.

'Hello', answered David. 'Mrs Johnson, I haven't got a family, have I?'

'No,' said Mrs Johnson, 'but you belong to our school family. We have lots of people in it. We live and work together every day, and we care about each other. You are part of our school family David.'

'Mmm', said David.

At hometime, David saw Mr Wilson, the next-door-neighbour, in his garden. David shouted over the fence.

'Hello, Mr Wilson. I haven't got a family, have I?'

'Oh yes you have', said Mr Wilson, walking towards the fence. 'You belong to the family of man. We all do. All people belong to the family of man.'

'That's silly', said David. 'First Auntie Barbara, then Mrs Brown, Mrs Johnson, and now you, all say I belong to a big family of people. How can all those people be my family. It's stupid.'

'Well, we can't all be wrong,' said Mr Wilson, 'aunts, teachers, and me. Just you think about it. A family is a group of people who all belong to each other. You, in the home next door, in your class, in your school, in the world, all belong to each other.'

'But I can't be expected to like everybody', argued David.

'Oh, you're not expected to *like* everyone. People with real brothers and sisters don't always *like* them all the time', said Mr Wilson. 'In a real family people care about each other, and look after each other, and try to help each other. Doesn't that happen in your home and in your class and in your school?'

'Yes', said David.

'Well, there you are then', said Mr Wilson. 'A family is a group of people who belong to each other in some way, and who care about each other. So, you do have a family: a home family, a school family, and a world family. When you belong to a family, you have a responsibility to look after the people in it. Make sure you do your bit', said Mr Wilson, and he turned round and walked into his own house.

David went in to his house and said to Auntie Barbara, 'I belong to a family: a family at home, a family at school, and a family of man.'

'We all do', said Auntie Barbara. 'I'm glad you know you have a family David.'

We all have those three families that David has. Let's make sure we care for the other people in our home family, our school family and our world family. Let's do what Mr Wilson told David to do, let's all 'do our bit' to help.

Prayer

Thank you, God, for our families.
Thank you for our family at home,
Thank you for our family at school,
Thank you for the family of man.
Teach us to care for people in our home family,
　　　our school family, and our world family.

Amen

Hymn
'The family of man' **C&P**

Dr Barnardo

Week 9   Family

Just imagine what it would be like if you had no house to live in, no bedroom, and no bed to sleep in. Just think what it would be like, if every night you went to sleep curled up in a cardboard box, like this one, with just old newspapers for blankets. Just think how cold and uncomfortable it would be outside in a street or a shop doorway. The cardboard would become wet and soggy every time it rained or snowed. The box and the newspapers would become dirty and smelly.

Yet, lots of boys and girls in big cities lived like that a hundred years ago. If a boy or girl's mother and father died, and there was no-one else to look after them, they simply had to live on the streets and beg for food to eat.

One night, about a hundred years ago, a man was walking through the streets of London, on his way home. He was walking up some steps near the river, when his foot kicked against something. The man looked to see what he had stumbled against and he saw that it was a big cardboard box, with what looked like a lot of rubbish inside. The man kicked the box out of the way, and as he did so he heard a noise like a cry. The sound seemed to be coming from inside the box. The man bent down, pulled aside some old newspapers, and there, huddled in the bottom of the box, was a small boy. He looked frightened.

'Please don't hurt me, mister', he said to the man.

'I'm not going to hurt you,' said the man, 'but what are you doing in there? You should be at home with your mother and father.'

'I ain't got no mother 'n father', answered the boy. 'I sleep 'ere every night, with me mates.'

'You mean there are others here, sleeping like this, with no homes to go to?' said the man, looking astonished.

'There are loads of us,' said the boy, 'shall I show you?' And he pointed out lots of cardboard boxes and piles of crumpled newspapers to the man. Each box and each heap of paper contained a sleeping boy.

'This is dreadful', said the man, 'you ought to be sleeping in proper beds, in proper houses, not out here in old boxes. I shall try to do something to help.' And the man walked away shaking his head.

The man went to see his friends. They were all important men in the city. The man himself was important, he was a doctor, his name was Dr Barnardo. He told his friends about the homeless boys, sleeping in cardboard boxes by the river.

'We must help those boys', said Dr Barnardo, 'they need beds, houses, food and shelter.'

'You're a fool, Barnardo', said his friends, 'those boys are street urchins.

They don't know how to behave in houses. If you gave them a house, with furniture, they'd only smash it up. They can't be trusted.'

'They could be trusted if they were given a chance', answered Barnardo. 'I'm going to give them that chance. I'm going to buy a house for them to live in.'

'You're wasting your money', said the friends.

But Dr Barnardo knew he wanted to help the boys. He went back the next night to talk to them again.

'Would you like to live in a house?' he asked.

'Would we like to live in a house!' answered the boys.

'Would you take care of the house?' asked Dr Barnardo.

'We would sir, if we had one', said the boys.

'Then I will buy a house for you', said Dr Barnardo; and he did.

The boys were overjoyed. They looked after the house, cleaned it and cared for it, so that it sparkled with cleanness and with happiness.

The friends of Dr Barnardo had to admit that they had been wrong. Soon Dr Barnardo bought another house in another part of London for some more boys, and girls, who had no homes of their own. The idea of the Dr Barnardo homes spread to other towns and cities, and before long, homeless children all over the country had homes to live in.

Today, Dr Barnardo is no longer alive, but his homes are here, in nearly every city and town. Thanks to Dr Barnardo and his kindness, children who have no mothers or fathers do not have to live in cardboard boxes on the streets, they are properly cared for and looked after, and have proper houses to live in.

Prayer

    Thank you, God, for the kindness of Dr Barnardo.
    We thank you for our houses and homes.
    We thank you for our beds and bedrooms.
    We pray that homeless people in other countries will be helped
            to find homes to live in, just as the homeless children
            in England were helped to have homes, by Dr Barnardo.

Hymn
'Cross over the road' **C&P**

A bill for mum   *Week 9   Family*

This week we have been thinking about families, and if I were to ask you who the most important person is in your family, I think lots of you would say it is your mum. On Sunday of course, it will be Mothering Sunday, or Mothers' Day as we often call it now. Mothering Sunday is the day when we think of our mums, and we try to make that day especially nice for them, as a thank you for all they do for us. In the old days, when quite young children went to work away from home, Mothering Sunday was the one day when they were allowed to go back home to see their mothers. They used to take small presents, perhaps a cake they had been allowed to bake, or some wild flowers they picked on the way to their mother's house. Lots of you will be giving your mum a small present on Sunday, and I know that most of you have made Mothers' Day cards. Some of them are here on display.*

Today I have a story for you about a boy and his mum.

John had seen a toy car in the shop window and he very much wanted to buy it for his collection. The car cost £1, and although John was given pocket money each week, he didn't get enough to buy the car. He only had 5p left from last week's money. He could save up for the car, he thought, but that would take some time, and by then the car might be sold to someone else. Anyway, he didn't want to wait, he wanted the car now.

John thought about the problem all day. He wondered how he could manage to get £1 in the shortest possible time. By teatime he had the answer. It was easy, why hadn't he thought of it earlier? All he had to do was work for it. He often did jobs for his mum or dad, and usually they paid him for helping. Then he had an even better idea; he would send his mum a bill. He had already done some jobs that week; he had helped his dad wash the car, and had washed up twice.

John went to get a piece of paper and a pencil. He wrote out the bill:

washing up	10p
shopping	20p
cleaning shoes	10p
washing car	30p
working hard at school	25p
	95p

Just right! With the 5p he had left from his pocket money, he would be able to buy the car the very next day. He put the piece of paper on the table, where he knew his mum would find it when she laid the table for tea. Then John went out to play.

A few minutes later, John's mum went to the table and saw the bill. She stood looking at it for a long time, with a serious look on her face. She felt a bit upset, because she knew that in a family you do lots of things for each other, because you care for each other, not because you want money.

She thought of all the things she had done for John because she loved him. She wondered how she could explain to him that people must do things for each other without always getting paid for it. Then she thought of a way to tell him.

John's mum also got a piece of paper and a pencil, and she wrote a bill for John. This is what she wrote.

Looking after you when you were a baby	0p
Looking after you when you were ill	0p
Taking you on holiday	0p
Giving you birthday parties	0p
Giving you presents, toys, books	0p
Giving you all your meals	0p
Giving you a warm, comfortable home	0p
total, for caring for you always – nothing.	

At teatime John came in and saw the piece of paper on his plate. He read the bill and he understood.

'I'm sorry, mum', he said.

'That's alright John,' said his mum, 'just remember there are things more important than money.'

John nodded.

By the way, he did buy the car for his collection. John saved all his pocket money for the next two weeks, and then bought the car.

I hope that you will all remember this weekend, all the many things your mums do for you! I hope you will remember to say thank you to your mums on Mothers' Day.

Prayer

Thank you, God, for our families, especially for our mothers.
Help us to do our best to show our mums how much we care,
by being thoughtful and helpful all the time,
not just on Mothers' day.

Amen

Hymn
'Join with us' **C&P**

On occasions such as Christmas, Mothering Sunday, Easter etc. when the whole school is engaged upon a common theme, I usually make a display of the children's greetings' cards. The children are always interested in seeing what others have made, and the displays provide a source of inspiration and ideas for cards, for both children and teachers. It is yet another simply way in which we can all share our ideas with each other.

The slave traders

Week 10 Freedom

Just imagine how you would feel if, one day, someone came along and took you away from your family and friends, and sold you as a slave: making you work hard all day long, doing jobs, and not giving you any spare time or letting you do anything you wanted to do. It would be terrible. Of course, that won't happen to you, because children are no longer sold as slaves. A man called William Wilberforce worked very hard, over 150 years ago, to make laws to stop slave trading. But, before those laws were passed things were very different from now, especially in countries like Africa.

One day an African boy wandered out of his village into the forest to search for a piece of wood for the drum he was making. By the end of the afternoon he had not returned to his hut in the village and his brothers and sisters were sent to look for him. They searched in all the places where he usually went, but he was nowhere to be seen. His brothers and sisters went back to the village with the news that they couldn't find him and in no time all the village men had formed a search party and they went out into the tropical forest to look for the boy. They thought he may have walked too far and got lost, or perhaps that he had been attacked by a wild animal and was lying injured somewhere. No-one dared to put into words the idea that he might have been captured by slave traders and that they would never see him again, but they all knew that it could have happened. Just before dark, when the men were tired and weary with searching, the boy's father found the leather necklace and ivory good luck charm that the boy always wore around his neck. It had been pulled from his neck and thrown onto the ground. There were no animal tracks nearby, and the men knew that the boy had been kidnapped by the slave traders.

The men, grown up though they were, began to weep at the thought of the dreadful life ahead for the boy whom they would never see again.

The slave traders had grabbed the boy they found in the forest and roped him to other boys and girls they had stolen from the nearby villages. The children were dragged through miles of tropical forest until they reached the sea. The children were given nothing to eat or drink, they were beaten if they did not walk quickly enough, they had rope burns on their arms and blisters and cuts on their feet. They were now a long way from their families and friends and were frightened and unhappy. The boy started to cry, but was hit across his face and told to stop.

When they reached the sea, the children saw a huge ship. They were crammed into small boats which took them out to the ship. When they were pulled on board still roped together, they were taken deep, deep, down into the depths of the ship and made to lie on the floor. Hundreds of kidnapped Africans were squashed together in the dark insides of the ship. And there they stayed, in dark, dirty, smelly conditions for many weeks. Many of the slaves became ill and some of them died. The boy, like most of the others, was desperately sea-sick, and had painful stomach ache. There was a little food, but not much, a little water, but not clean. The boy cried for his mother, his home and his village. They were now a long way away and he knew he would not see them again.

At last the rocking, heaving ship, slowed and stopped. The slaves, now chained together, were brought up into the blinding sunlight they had not seen for weeks, and pushed along planks to the ground. They were in America.

Now they were taken into market places and sold. As soon as an owner bought a slave, the slave was branded with the owner's mark. The mark was put onto his back with a red-hot iron. Everyone now knew who the slave belonged to. The slave had no rights, but had to do exactly what the owner told him to. It was no use running away, as a slave was bound to be caught sooner or later and would then be killed, or have a foot cut off to stop him running away again.

Some owners were kind and fair to their slaves, but many were unkind, cruel and thoughtless, treating their slaves with less respect than they treated their animals.

We do not know what happened to the boy after he got off the ship. We *do* know that he would have been sold, and branded, and that he would never have been free to do anything he wanted to do. He would have lived the rest of his life belonging to his owners. Perhaps they were quite kind to him, or perhaps they were unkind, cruel owners.

When William Wilberforce saw these awful things happening to slaves, and when he realised that people were being kidnapped and sold as slaves, he worked very hard to make new laws to stop slave trading. He wanted *all* men to be free and wanted all men to have human dignity and to belong to themselves, not cruel masters. After a great deal of hard work, William Wilberforce and his friends had the new laws passed, and all slaves under British law were freed.

We are glad that we do not live in cruel times like those of the slave-trading days. We must remember as we grow up always to treat other people, no matter who they are, with respect, so that we are never cruel or unkind.

Prayer

Thank you, God, for our freedom.
Help us to use our freedom well, and to make sure as we grow up
that we treat everyone fairly.

Amen

Hymn
'Tomorrow' **SFJ**

Robot City
Week 10   Freedom

In our last assembly, we heard about something that happened over one hundred and fifty years ago. Today we are going to pretend that we can more forward 150 years into the future.

Everything is different. The world is full of robots who do all the jobs that people do now. The people have become lazy because the only job they now have to do is care for the robots. Because the people are lazy, they do not look after the robots; they do not oil them or clean them or polish their metal parts. Many robots have become rusty and broken.

The robots are controlled by men who must remember to switch off the control boxes when the robots have finished their work.

One dark night, some thieves broke into a factory. They found the robot control box, and began playing with the robots, switching them on and off, making them dance and making them speak. Suddenly the factory alarm bells rang out, and the thieves dropped the control box in a mad dash to get away before being caught by the robot police. They box lay forgotten on the floor as the robot police searched for the thieves.

An hour later all was calm and quiet again and one of the factory robots noticed the control box still lying on the floor. It was still switched on, and the robots were still activated. The robot picked it up and began to work the other robots. It was the very first time that the robots had been controlled by one of their own kind, instead of by a man. Automanence, the robot who had found the control box, had been programmed to think, to work out manufacturing problems in the factory. He now used his thinking ability to work out a plan to teach mankind a lesson.

The next morning when the factory doors automatically opened, people standing nearby were astonished to see the factory robots marching down the steps and into the street, led by Automanence and the control box.

'The robots are escaping,' shouted the people, 'fetch the robot police.' In no time an army of robot police marched up the street from the police centre, but they could go no further than Automanence and his robots. Automanence de-activated the police robots and left them standing stiffly and useless in the street. Automanence and his robots marched on through the city. At every house or office or factory window, Automanence stopped and using the control box de-activated every robot in every building, and made them unable to move. Soon there was not a working robot left in the entire city.

The people were dismayed. They tried to mend their robots, using screw-drivers and hammers. They tried to reprogramme the robots using their computers, but nothing worked. The whole city was at a standstill.

The people began gathering together outside the Technocentre, asking each other what was to be done.

'We must somehow get back the control box', they said. 'We must disarm the robots before they control or kill us', they said. 'But how?' they said.

Without having any definite plan, the people began to march towards the street where Automanence had last been seen. He was gone. Automanence and the active robots were now marching on other cities with a clear plan. In every city and town they de-activated half the robots and programmed the other half to march to a new city, where in turn, they de-activated half of those robots and programmed the other half to march to yet another city.

In a matter of hours the robots had stopped all work in the whole of the country. Automanence and the active robots marched into the capital city. Outside the doors of the country's main Technocentre, they stopped. The Prime Minister and members of the people's government stepped outside.

Automanence spoke, 'We have brought your country to a stop. We will do no more work. You will work. You will learn to mend and care for your robots. You have treated us badly. You have not cared. You must learn. We will not hurt you. Please do not hurt us.'

The people listened to this speech and understood.

'Show us you will care for us properly,' said Automanence, 'and we will work for you again.'

The Prime Minister and the people's government organised the people into working teams, and the renovation of the robots began. Parts were oiled, cleaned, greased, sharpened and polished. Soon the robots were shin-ing, gleaming, glistening and sparkling. When they were all ready, all over the country, Automanence spoke again.

'I will activate all the robots again', he said, 'but I will keep the control box. If ever you do not care for your robots again, I will once more switch the robots off, but if there is a next time, I might not switch them on again.'

The people promised that they would care for all their machines in future, and Automanence and his robots switched on the whole country's robots again. The cities hummed with working machines, and never again did the people allow their machines to become broken and rusty.

If ever *you* have a robot to work for you, I hope you will look after him!

Prayer

Dear God, thank you for machines,
which help us with all our work at home and at school.
Thank you for the freedom from work that machines can give us.
Help us to look after all the machines we use
so that we do not break or damage them.

Amen

Hymn

'Thank you Lord' **C&P**

Free to choose   *Week 10   Freedom*

Once upon a time there were two young men who were friends. They always spent their spare time together. One of the young men was usually quite a cheerful person, but the other one was always grumbling.

'It's not fair,' he said one day, 'I can never do what I want to do. I wish I could be a footballer.'

'You could be if you wanted to', said the other young man. 'You could play football in your spare time and you could join a good amateur team.'

'No, I couldn't,' said the first young man, 'anyway, I wish I could travel abroad, that's what I would really like to do.'

'Well you could do that', said the second young man. 'You could save up and go abroad on holiday, or you could even get a job and work abroad if you wanted to.'

'No, I couldn't', said the first young man.

The conversation went on like this for quite some time, the first young man complaining that he couldn't do things he wanted to do, and the second young man saying that anything was possible if the man really wanted to do something.

The next day the two friends met again, and the first young man began to moan, and complain again. 'It's not fair', he said, 'nothing exciting ever happens to me.'

The second young man pulled a box out of his pocket. 'Look', he said, 'I've brought you a present to cheer you up.'

The first young man's face lit up into a smile. 'For me?' he asked, and he began to open the box. A minute later the smile disappeared as he looked into an empty box.

'There's nothing in it,' he said, 'that's a mean trick to play on me, it's not fair.'

'Now just you listen to me', said the second young man. 'That box, which you think is empty, is full of freedom; your freedom. You keep grumbling that you can't do this, that and the other; but you are free to try to do anything at all.

'You are not a slave. You have a brain and you are free to look for opportunities. You live in a country where you are free to think what you want. You are free to be what you want. No-one owns you like a slave.

'You are not a machine like a robot, controlled by others. You control yourself. You are free to be lazy or hardworking; free to be good or bad; free to be helpful or a nuisance; free to be happy or miserable.

'I will tell you a story', went on the second young man. 'There was once a fat house dog and a starving wolf who met in the forest one night. The starving wolf wanted food and the house dog told him he could come home and work for the master. The wolf thought it was a good idea. If he worked hard, the master would feed him. He set off to follow that fat house dog, but as he trotted through the forest, he noticed a bare patch on the house dog's neck.

'What is that bald patch?' asked the wolf.

'Oh, it's nothing', answered the house dog.

'It must be something,' said the wolf, 'what is it?'

'Oh, it's just where my collar and chain rubs my fur away', said the house dog.

The wolf stopped suddenly in his tracks.

'Do you mean to tell me that you are chained?' asked the wolf, in disbelief.

'Yes, but only during the day', said the dog. 'My master sets me free at night!'

'I'm off,' said the wolf, 'I would rather be hungry and free than fat and chained.'

And with a swish of his tail the wolf went back to his freedom in the forest.

'Now just you think about all that', said the second young man. 'Use your freedom well', and he walked away from the first young man, who stood there staring at him. But he *had* listened, I am pleased to say.

We all have freedom. We are not slaves or robots. We have brains and it is up to us to decide how to use them. We can make our lives useful and exciting, or dull and boring. I know which I am going to choose!

Prayer

Thank you, God, for our freedom:
freedom to think, freedom to make of our lives what we can.
Help us never to treat anyone else like a slave.
Help us never to treat anyone else like a machine with no feeling.
Help us to use our freedom well.

Amen

Hymn

'Praise the Lord in everything' **C&P**

The wind and the sun

Week 11   Sunshine

adapted from Aesop

One day last week I felt quite fed up and miserable. It had rained hard all day and was still raining when I got home from school. I had hoped to go outside and do some work in my garden, but it was too wet and I wasn't able to.

The next day was sunny and warm. The birds were singing, I saw new leaves beginning to grow on the trees, and flowers beginning to grow in the gardens. I felt very happy. I think I felt so cheerful because the sun was shining and making me feel better. The sun is very good at making people feel cheerful, it is very strong in lots of ways. I have a story for you today which tells of the sun one day proving its strength.

It all started when the wind and the sun were having an argument. They were always arguing; each thought himself stronger, braver, better than the other.

'I'm much stronger than you', said the wind. 'I'm so powerful, I can blow down buildings and uproot trees. You can't do that, sun. All you do is sit in the sky all day and shine. There's nothing powerful about that.'

'I'm a good deal stronger than you think', answered the sun. 'I'm stronger than you when I want to be.'

'Then prove it', said the wind. 'I challenge you to a contest to prove which of us is stronger. There's a man down there on the road, wearing a big, black overcoat. Whichever of us can make him take his coat off first, is the stronger. We'll take it in turns until one of us wins.'

'Right!' said the sun. 'You can go first.'

'Good!' said the wind.

The sun hid himself behind a cloud, and the wind gathered all his strength.

He whirled and swirled, huffed and puffed and shrieked and roared. The man looked anxiously up at the sky, buttoned his coat up to the neck, turned up his coat collar, thrust his chin down and his hands into his pockets. He then walked quickly and firmly into the wind.

The wind blew even stronger. He howled and swooped around the man, making the coat flap and whip around the man's legs. The man again looked up at the sky, took his hands out of his pockets and gripped his arms around himself.

The wind by now was angry. He tore a tree out of the ground and hurled it down in front of the man. The man, frightened, jumped into the hedge bottom and lay huddled on the ground, tightly wrapped up in his coat.

The wind blustered away into the rumbling distance and shouted for the sun to have his turn.

Slowly, slowly, the air became still. The scurrying clouds behind which the sun was hiding, slowed down to a soft fluff. The sun gently slid from behind the clouds, and hung, quite still and quiet and golden in the sky. The man crept from his place of safety and carried on along the road. The sun shone and glowed red. The man loosened his collar and undid his coat buttons. The sun sparkled and sizzled. The man took out his handkerchief and mopped his brow. The sun blazed with a shimmering heat. The man stopped walking, . . . and took off his coat! The sun smiled warmly.

'You see,' he said to the wind, 'you don't need to make a lot of noise about being strong and powerful. You can be strong quietly and calmly.' But the wind wasn't listening. He was a bad loser and he had blown himself away in a huff.

Sometimes people are like the wind or the sun. Some people like to make a lot of noise and let everyone know they are there. Other people like to quietly get on with their jobs. I wonder which sort of person you are? Sometimes the people who make the most noise, often have the least important things to say!

Prayer

Thank you, God, for sunshine.
Thank you for springtime.
Thank you for longer days, warmer weather, and everything alive.
Thank you for springtime, sunshine, happiness.

Amen

Hymn
'I love the sun' **SSL**

The donkey and his shadow

Week 11 Sunshine

adapted from Aesop

You may have noticed that when you are outside playing, in sunny weather, there is always something with you on the ground. Sometimes it is long, sometimes it is short, and its feet are nearly always touching your feet. It goes away when the sun goes in, and comes back when the sun comes out. What is it?

Yes, it is your shadow. In the middle of the day when the sun is high in the sky, your shadow is very short, but in the early morning and late evening when the sun is low in the sky, your shadow can be very long, much longer than you.

There was once a donkey who used to work, together with his owner, carrying people and packages to where they wanted to go; rather like a donkey taxi service.

One day a young man asked to be taken to a nearby town. He wanted to ride, not walk, and he wanted his parcels carrying as well. The donkey's owner settled on a price for the young man to pay for the journey, and within a few minutes they all set off; the young man riding on the donkey and the owner walking alongside the donkey, leading him by the reins.

By the middle of the day, the three were about half way to the town and they decided to stop and have a rest. The owner led the donkey to the grass at the side of the road. The young man climbed down from the donkey's back, and got out his lunch from one of the parcels.

The weather was very hot, and there was no shade anywhere, so the young man sat down in the donkey's shadow.

'Just a minute!' shouted the owner. 'You can't sit there. That's my shadow.'

'It's not your shadow,' said the young man. 'It's my shadow. I hired this donkey for the day, so it's my shadow.'

'Rubbish!' shouted the owner. 'You hired the donkey, but you didn't hire his shadow.'

'It's my shadow', shouted the young man.

'No it's not. It's my shadow', shouted the owner.

In no time at all the two men were having a terrible argument, and in two minutes more the argument had grown into a quarrel and the quarrel had grown into a fight.

They pushed and punched, thumped and kicked, each of them believing that the donkey's shadow was his, and each of them determined to sit in the small shadow.

The two men were so busy quarrelling and fighting that they didn't see what was happening. The small shadow was slowly moving away from them.

It moved from the grass at the side of the road, onto the road itself. Then the shadow began to run down the road, with the donkey of course, and by the time the two quarrelling men had noticed that the donkey had gone, he and his shadow had rounded the bend in the road and were well on their way to town.

'They're not having my shadow,' said the donkey to himself, 'they can fight over their own shadows. I'm taking mine away.'

The young man and the donkey's owner had to walk together all the rest of the way to the town.

The donkey showed the two men that fighting did not help either of them. He also showed them that shadows cannot be bought. Shadows come with sunshine and sunshine brings shadows. Shadows as well as sunshine are part of our lives. Perhaps the next time you are playing out in the sun, you can look at your shadow and your friends' shadows. You could see what you can find out about shadows.

Prayer
>Thank you, God, for springtime sunshine.
>Thank you for our shadows.
>Help us to remember that shadows as well as sunshine
>>are part of our lives.
>Help us to remember that beyond the shadows the sun is shining.
>>>>>>*Amen*

Hymn
'I have seen the golden sunshine' **SSL**

Every cloud has a silver lining
Week 11   Sunshine

My grandma used to have lots of different sayings for lots of different occasions, and one of the things she used to say was, 'Every cloud has a silver lining.' She always used to say it if someone had heard some bad news, or if something had just gone wrong. One day I said to her, 'Grandma, why do you say "Every cloud has a silver lining"; what does it mean?'

'I'll tell you a story', she said.

Once upon a time there was a strange old woman who lived in a tiny cottage at the end of a lane. She said she was ninety nine years old, and she said she could make magic spells. She had a wrinkled brown face and twinkling brown eyes. She had white hair which she wore in two long plaits, wound round over her head. She wore long black dresses with white petticoats, and always a billowing, snowy-white apron. She was a kind old woman, and always had a cheerful smile and a friendly word for everyone.

Each morning she walked through the village to the bakery to buy a loaf of bread, and each morning she said a cheery 'Good morning. The sun is shining brightly', to everyone she met. On sunny days, of course, that greeting was all right; but on cloudy, dull, rainy or foggy days it sounded a little strange and people would say 'Oh no, Mistress Blackwhite, the sun is not shining today.'

'Oh yes it is', she would reply. 'You may not be able to see it, but up in the sky, above the clouds, the sun is shining brightly. The clouds are in the way, that's all.'

One particular winter, everything seemed to go wrong in the village. Everyone seemed to be having bad luck, sadness and unhappiness. The squire's daughter had an accident on her horse and hurt her back so badly that she couldn't walk at all. Farmer Brown's cows became ill and stopped giving milk. Mrs Henshaw's geese escaped through a hole in the hedge and got lost. A huge old beech tree at the corner of the green was struck by lightning, and crashed down onto one of the cottages. Luckily no-one was hurt, but the cottage was in ruins and the lane was blocked for days, with rubble and branches. The weather was awful. Roads turned to mud, the river burst its banks and flooded eleven houses in Weaver's Row. Everyone was miserable, down-hearted and unhappy. It was just as though a big, black, heavy cloud had descended upon the village, and nothing could move it.

Each morning during that dreadful winter, Mistress Blackwhite walked to the bakery as usual, and each day she said to everyone, 'Good morning, the sun is shining brightly.'

'Silly old woman', said some people.

'She doesn't know what she's saying', said others.

'Ignore her, take no notice', said some.

'But the bad luck won't last forever', said Mistress Blackwhite. 'Try to look on the bright side of things. Try to be as cheerful as possible. It'll make you feel better. Remember, the sun is shining above the clouds.'

But the people wouldn't listen. They would not and could not look on the bright side of things. They felt they had every right to be miserable and unhappy, because everything was going wrong.

Mistress Blackwhite watched in dismay as everyone in the village became more and more unhappy, grumpy and disheartened. 'I must do something to cheer everyone up', thought Mistress Blackwhite. 'Soon things will get better, I just know they will.'

That evening, Mistress Blackwhite stood at her kitchen stove and stirred a strange, silver liquid in a circular, silvery saucepan. She stirred and stirred for seven hours and seven minutes, then she poured the silver liquid into a basin and left it to cool. When it was cold it had set into a solid, silvery shape and Mistress Blackwhite tipped it out onto her chopping board and chopped it into a million pieces like silver confetti. Then she put on her coat, and, as the cockerel crowed, and the first fingers of daylight reached across the sky, she went out and threw the sparkling pieces of silver confetti in a shimmering crescent high into the air. Then she went home.

Later that morning, when the people came out of their houses, into a cloudy, rainy day, they noticed that every cloud in the sky had a bright, shining, silver lining, which caught the sparkling golden rays of the sun, shining high above them.

'Look', they all said. 'The sun is shining above the clouds, and every cloud has a silver lining. It must mean that soon our luck will change and everything will be all right again.'

Mistress Blackwhite smiled to herself.

Each day the people became happier, brighter and more cheerful. Soon the grey clouds with the silver lining rolled away and the springtime came. The bad luck of the village changed to good luck. The squire's daughter learned to smile again from her chair. The cows gave milk again, the geese were found, and the roads and fences mended.

Ever since that time, whenever things go wrong, people say 'Every cloud has a silver lining', because however sad they are, people know that the sun will shine again, and that if they are brave and cheerful, things will get better.

Prayer

    Dear God, please help us to be cheerful
        and to look on the bright side of things.
    Help us to remember that every cloud has a silver lining,
        and that when things go wrong we must try to be brave
        and cheerful.
    Help us to remember that the sun is always shining above the clouds.

Amen

Hymn
'Sing for Joy' **SFJ**

The Easter rabbit

This weekend, as I have been driving about in my car, and walking in my garden, I have seen lots of signs of the coming of spring. I have also seen signs of spring here, in and around school. In our school garden there are shoots beginning to poke up out of the ground, there are buds appearing on our trees. Inside school, there are seeds beginning to grow in pots, spring flowers are being brought to school, spring pictures are on the walls. And soon it will be Easter.

Easter and spring always come at nearly the same time.

There are many folk stories about spring and Easter, and today I'm going to tell you one about an Easter rabbit.

He had been asleep in his burrow in the warren, in the bottom field for quite some time, and now he was awake. He crept along the maze of underground tunnels until he reached his entrance hole, and he poked his nose and whiskers outside.

It was dark and bitterly cold. The wind whistled across the short, spiky grass and brought with it slivers of sleet. The rabbit shivered and hurried back to his warm nest. He went back to sleep.

A little later the rabbit woke again, and once more burrowed to the end of the tunnel and looked out at the world. This time the world was grey. The sky was grey, the clouds were grey. The ground looked grey, and the trees looked gaunt and black. It was cold.

The rabbit crept out of the round hole in the banking and scuttled along the hedge bottom at the edge of the field. Everything looked dead. The hedge, the field, even the big old beech tree at the corner, all looked dead. The rabbit felt miserable, cold and unhappy, as he turned to go back to his burrow.

As he turned he noticed a streak of pink light being drawn across the sky. It was followed by a stripe of silver, and another band of bright turquoise blue. The sky looked so beautiful that the rabbit stopped in his tracks to watch the changing light of the dawn.

Then, to his amazement, he saw a curious floating creature who wafted towards him.

'Who are you?' whispered the rabbit.

'I am Oestre,' said the creature, 'I am of the dawn and spring. You think our world is dead, but come with me and look.' She showed the rabbit the hedge, and in the dawn light, he could see that it was not dead but that it was covered with tiny green buds. He saw new blades of green grass in the hedge bottom, and the small yellow buds of celandines and primroses. She took him to the beech tree, and he saw the new green leaves, tightly furled, waiting for the spring sunshine to make them open. She showed him the blackthorn blossom, sparkling white, and the yellow nodding daffodils in the nearby gardens. Oestre showed the rabbit spring.

'The world is not dead,' shouted the rabbit happily, 'it is very much alive, and it's beautiful', and he hopped away to tell all the other animals about the growing life in their fields and woods.

The rabbit felt so happy that the world was not dead and that the spring had come, that he decided it would be his job every year to tell the world when spring had arrived. He didn't want anyone else to feel as miserable and unhappy as he had done on that day when he thought everything was grey and dead.

And so each year, the Easter rabbit brings everyone an egg, to show that new life is here; to show that spring has come.

Perhaps, if you are very lucky, the Easter rabbit may have time to visit you, and bring you an egg!

Prayer
Thank you, God, for Easter and springtime.
Thank you for new life and new growth.
Thank you for the seasons which come round each year.

Amen

Hymn
'Who put the colours in the rainbow' **C&P**

The chocolate eggs
Week 12   Easter

The shops are full of chocolate Easter eggs, at the moment. At the weekend I went to the sweet shop near my home, and one whole wall of the shop was filled with an Easter egg display. There were tiny sugar eggs to buy by the quarter, there was a huge chocolate egg decorated with sugar flowers and leaves, in a big basket, and there were eggs of every size, in between. Some were in coloured boxes, some were wrapped in shiny coloured paper, some had bars of chocolate or individual chocolates with them as well. All of them looked absolutely delicious. I chose a Smarties egg and a Yorkie Bar egg, for my niece and nephew. I expect most of you are hoping that someone will buy you a chocolate egg for Easter.

It was very easy for me to go into the shop and buy those two eggs at the weekend, but if I had gone to that same shop forty-five years ago, it wouldn't have been so easy. The shop was there, but you couldn't just walk in and buy sweets, like you can today.

Joan and Richard were two children who lived near the sweet shop, forty-five years ago. Every Saturday their mum gave them pocket money, and every Saturday they sat on the back doorstep deciding how to spend it. Sometimes they went to see the Saturday afternoon children's film at the pictures. Sometimes they bought comics, a colouring book, or pencils or paints. Sometimes they spent it on sweets; but if they chose sweets, they had a problem. You see, forty-five years ago, Britain was at war, and many foods including sweets, were rationed. That meant that each person was only allowed a certain amount, no matter how much money they had. Everyone had a ration book, a little book which contained tiny, tear-out coupons. Every bar of chocolate, or bag of sweets had to be paid for with money and with coupons. The coupons allowed you to have a few ounces of sweets each week. No-one could have more than that. Even if you were rich and had lots of money, you couldn't buy extra sweets, you could only buy what your coupons allowed.

One Saturday, Joan and Richard went into the sweet shop and as they were looking around, they saw two lovely, big, chocolate Easter eggs on display.

'Ooh! Don't they look good', sighed Joan.

'How much?' asked Richard.

'Ah! Too much for you lad', said the shopkeeper. 'I doubt we'll sell them. Folk haven't the coupons to be able to buy luxuries like these any more. You'd do better to save your coupons, you and your sister, and buy ordinary chocolate bars.'

'Yes, but bars are not eggs, are they?' answered Richard. 'Come on Joan, let's go home', and the two children went out of the shop, and home, to tell their mum about the Easter eggs.

'Well, I'm afraid we haven't enough coupons to buy chocolate eggs', said their mum.

'The man said he'd not be able to sell them', said Joan. 'He said we'd do better to buy ordinary chocolate, instead of eggs; but it's not the same, is it mum? Eggs are better.'

'How badly do you want an Easter egg?' asked the children's mum.

Joan and Richard were so surprised at the question, that neither of them answered.

'We haven't enough coupons to buy Easter eggs,' went on their mum, 'so we'll buy chocolate, and we'll make Easter eggs. But, if you want to do that, you'll have to do without sweets for one whole month, and you'll have to save the coupons, so that we can buy the chocolate to make the eggs.'

'Make the eggs?' said Joan and Richard. 'How can we make the eggs?'

'I have an Easter egg mould', answered their mum. 'We'll melt the chocolate and pour it into the egg mould. But remember, if you want eggs, you'll have to do without any sweets for a month, to save your coupons.'

The children decided that it would be worth doing without sweets, and saving coupons, for a whole month, if it meant they could have a chocolate egg for Easter.

The next four weeks were very, very hard. Each Saturday the children saved their pocket money, and their coupons. It was hard walking past the sweet shop and not going in. Twice they wanted sweets so badly they felt like giving in, and using their coupons, but the sight of those chocolate eggs made them think again.

At the end of the month, they went with their mum to the shop, and bought bars of chocolate with their saved money and saved coupons.

'My, you've been saving up well', commented the shop keeper.

They took the chocolate home, and helped their mum to melt it in a basin over a pan of hot water. The inside of the mould was coated with chocolate four times to make four separate egg halves. When the chocolate had set, the children's mum carefully took away the mould, and stuck the halves together with more melted chocolate. Last of all, she wrote 'Richard' on one egg, and 'Joan' on the other with white icing, and so the children had eggs for Easter.

I hope you have some chocolate eggs for Easter. When you are eating them, remember that children have not always been as lucky as you.

Prayer
> Thank you, God, for all the good things we have at Easter time.
> Teach us to share what we have, and not to be greedy.
>
> *Amen*

Hymn
'Thank you Lord' **C&P**

The Easter story   *Week 12   Easter*

This week in school, many of you have been making Easter cards, Easter bonnets, Easter baskets and Easter gifts, and here on this table is a display of some of the things you have made.* You will see how spring-like the display looks. There is lots of yellow and green, the colours of spring, and there are daffodils, primroses, lambs, eggs, and chickens; all signs of new life.

In the winter everything looked dead, but now in the spring we can see that everything is not dead, it is all very much alive. The gardens, fields, farms, trees and hedgerows are all full of new life.

Alive, when we thought it was dead.

Alive when they thought he was dead, was how the first Christians found Jesus on that first Easter Day.

Jesus knew that he must go into the City of Jerusalem, even though there were powerful men there, who did not like him. Jesus knew that one of his friends would give him away, and that he would be killed.

Jesus and his friends, the disciples, met together outside the City gate. One of the friends found a donkey for Jesus to ride on, and they all set off into the city together. On the way, people waved and cheered at Jesus, 'Hosanna,' they shouted, 'praise Him'. These people were pleased and happy to see Jesus. They believed he was a King who would one day save them, so they treated him like a King. 'Hosanna, Hosanna', they cheered, and waved branches of palm trees, and spread leaves of the palm trees at the donkey's feet, so that Jesus the King would have a carpet to walk on. As the procession moved towards Jerusalem, more and more people joined it, all shouting, all waving, and all happy. The procession stopped outside the temple and Jesus went inside to think and to pray.

The sight that met his eyes when he walked in through the temple doorway, horrified him. Here in the temple courtyard, where all should have been peace and quiet, it was like a market place, with people, crowds, stalls, buying and selling.

'These people have forgotten this is God's house', said Jesus. 'Stop', he shouted to them all, 'this is not a market place, it is a temple', but no-one took any notice and the noise went on. Jesus strode into the courtyard, grabbed two tables and tipped them over. He ran to the stalls and overturned them. He threw the money onto the floor. Adults, children, cats, dogs, goats, hens and horses scattered in all directions, and left the courtyard. The priests were angry with Jesus for interfering, but he didn't care; he had done what he knew was right. He turned and went out of the temple courtyard, out of Jerusalem and back to Bethany.

A few days later, Jesus decided to give a supper and talk to all his disciples. A friend lent Jesus a large upstairs room, big enough for a table at which all twelve of the disciples could sit. Peter and John prepared the food, and soon all the other disciples arrived. Jesus told them how much he cared about them all, and that soon he would have to leave them, but that they must all be very brave. Jesus knew that very soon now he would die.

After the supper, all the friends went to a place called the Garden of Gethsemane, because it was a quiet place, and Jesus wanted to pray. The disciples lay down against the trees, and were soon asleep; all except one, called Judas, who crept away to tell the soldiers where Jesus was.

The stillness of the garden was broken by the sudden noise of the soldiers. The disciples awoke, frightened, and looked around them to see soldiers, pointing, shouting, and waving spears. Then they saw Judas showing the soldiers who Jesus was; they saw the soldiers grab him and march him away.

The next day Jesus was taken to a hill outside the city, and nailed to a cross. He was left there to die. Later in the day, the disciples gently took down the body, wrapped it in fine cloth, and laid it in a cave in a beautiful garden. They rolled a huge stone over the entrance of the cave so that no-one could disturb Jesus's body. Then they went away.

Two days later, one of Jesus's friends, Mary Magdalene, went back to the cave, but was astonished to see that the stone had been rolled away. The cave was empty. She ran to tell Peter and John. They too came to look. Mary was right, the stone had been rolled away and the body was gone. Peter and John went away to tell the others, but Mary stayed in the garden. She saw a man walking towards her. He must be the gardener, thought Mary. Perhaps he knows what happened to Jesus's body. The man came nearer.

'Why are you crying?' he asked.

'I'm crying because I'm looking for Jesus. Do you know where he is?'

The man just said, 'Mary', and she knew at once who he was. It was Jesus. He was not dead. He was alive and he had spoken to her.

'Go and tell the others. I am alive', he said. Mary, happily, did as he asked.

At Easter time, Christians are happy because Jesus, whom they thought was dead, is alive.

At Easter time, people everywhere are happy, because the spring is here, and all that seemed dead, is alive.

Prayer

    Dear God, thank you for the new life of Easter time.
    Thank you for Easter flowers, Easter eggs, Easter holidays,
        and Easter happiness.

Amen

Hymn
'Praise Him' **C&P**

*The display included the children's cards, gifts, and 'egg containers'. The Easter display, without any pre-planning, always has a fresh, spring-like quality. In this particular assembly, I included Easter bonnets, which the mothers of the youngest children had made for the Easter Bonnet Parade. These were 'modelled', much to the delight of the rest of the school. (See also footnote on page 127.)

Summer Term

The garden flowers

One of the best things about this time of year is the flowers. Everywhere, in the hedgerows and the countryside, in people's gardens and even in the cities and towns, flowers are growing. I always think of March and April as yellow months, because of all the yellow flowers that grow in spring; the primroses and daffodils, and the yellow forsythia.

Perhaps we could try to fill our school with flowers this week, because it is the first week of the summer term. If everyone brought just one daffodil, or one twig of forsythia, or one tulip, we would soon have lots of flowers to decorate our school with.*

Bringing flowers reminds me of a story about two old ladies I know.

The two ladies live one at each side of a long street of houses. They are both widows, and they both live on their own. Their children have grown up and gone to live in houses of their own.

So, in lots of ways, the two old ladies are very much alike, but they are not alike in everything. One of them lives in a house with a garden full of flowers, and the other lives in a house with no garden.

The two old ladies don't know each other very well. They know each other's names and they say 'Good morning' or 'Good afternoon' to each other when they meet, but somehow they've never managed to get to know each other better than that, probably because they were on different sides of the road.

One day the lady in the house without a garden became ill. She woke up in the morning with a dreadful headache, and with aches and pains in her arms and legs as well.

'Oh dear!' she thought as she woke up. 'I was going to do so many things today. There's the washing to do, and some shopping to get; but I'm not feeling well enough to do any jobs. I think I'll have to stay in bed this morning.'

So that's exactly what she did. She didn't get out of bed at all. She didn't bring in the milk from her doorstep. She didn't collect the newspaper from the letterbox where it was sitting, half in and half out of her house. She didn't even open any of her curtains.

By lunchtime, the other lady living opposite had noticed the milk on the step, the newspaper in the letterbox and the closed curtains, and she wondered if the owner of the house was all right. But she didn't want to make a fuss, so she didn't do anything about it.

The next day, the lady who was poorly felt even worse. She hadn't had anything to eat now for a whole day, and when she tried to get out of bed, she felt wobbly and sick and dizzy. She fell back into her bed again feeling quite frightened. What should she do? She couldn't get up to telephone for the doctor, or to go round and ask her next door neighbour to get him. She felt so frightened because she was on her own and there was no-one to help her, that she started to cry.

The lady living opposite looked across the street again that morning. This time she noticed that at the old lady's house there were two bottles of milk on the doorstep, two newspapers sticking out of the letter box, and no curtains opened. Now she felt sure that something was wrong. She telephoned the police to explain that she thought something might be wrong with the old lady.

The police came quickly and sent for an ambulance. The old lady was taken to hospital. While she was in hospital the other lady wondered what she could do to help, but she couldn't think of anything except going to the hospital to visit. She picked some flowers from her garden and set off to catch the bus to visit the old lady.

'Hello', she said when she walked in to the ward. 'I'm sorry to hear you're poorly. I've brought some flowers from my garden to cheer you up.'

'Oh, thank you', said the old lady. 'You always have such lovely flowers in your garden. I wish I had a garden to grow flowers in.'

And in that moment, the lady from the house opposite knew exactly what she could do to help.

In a few days'time, when the old lady came out of hospital and went home again, her new friend from across the road called in with a bunch of flowers, to welcome her home. From that day on the friendship grew, and the lady with the garden full of flowers shared them with the lady who had no garden to grow them in.

Sharing the flowers helped the friendship along, between those two old ladies. Sharing always helps friendship to grow. Perhaps if you have a garden, and your mum or dad will let you bring a flower, we can all share our flowers here at school.

Prayer

> Thank you, God, for springtime flowers.
> Thank you for the happy feeling that flowers can give us.
> Thank you for the beauty of springtime flowers.
>
> *Amen*

Hymn
'All the flowers are waking' **SSL**

For this assembly, the beginnings of a display table were made ready in the hall. This held spring 'colours', some spring flowers, labelled for identification, and books about spring/flowers. The whole was backed with pictures and posters of various spring flowers. The children were encouraged – with their parents' permission, to bring a few spring flowers from their gardens for the display, which grew as the week progressed. It was stressed that the children should not pick wild flowers at all, or garden flowers without permission. In areas where children could not bring flowers, the ready-made display would suffice.

The Farndale daffodils   *Week 1   Flowers*

I like to have flowers in my home, and here in school as well. This week we have a lot of flowers in school, because we've been bringing them to decorate our school with. Sometimes it's right to pick flowers. If there are lots of flowers in our own garden, it's good to bring some of them indoors so that we can enjoy them inside as well as outside. Some flowers are grown especially for cutting; those are the flowers we see in florists' shops. But wild flowers are always best left growing where they are, so that lots of people can enjoy them.

When I was a little girl, I lived in a house quite near to a wood. When we were not at school, all my friends and I used to play in the wood. It was a good place for playing hide and seek, climbing trees, and making dens. We thought it was a huge, magical forest. In fact it was quite a small wood, and all our houses and gardens were built round the edge of it, so that when we were playing there, our mums or dads could hear us and see us and they knew we were safe.

In the wintertime we didn't play in it much. The weather was often cold and dark so we had to stay in. But, in the springtime, we moved into the wood again. There was an old hollow tree trunk that you could climb right inside; and where the wood met one of the garden fences, there was a tree with a huge low sloping branch that you could either climb up, or throw an old blanket over to make a tent.

In the springtime, the wood was filled with bluebells, growing wild under the trees. It was even more magical at that time of year when everywhere you looked was blue instead of green. We used to pick great armfuls of the flowers to take back home and put in jam jars on the sunny kitchen window-sills. Of course, we didn't think of what was going to happen!

The other day I met a friend of mine called Tom, who lives in a beautiful place in North Yorkshire called Farndale. We started talking about what we used to do when we were children, and I told Tom about how my friends and I used to play in bluebell wood, and how lovely it was, and what good fun we had.

Tom told me that when he was a child, he and his friends used to play in the daffodil woods by the stream in Farndale. He told me about how lovely it was and what good fun they all had. The only difference between my bluebell wood and his daffodil wood, was that my friends and I had picked the flowers in our wood; but Tom and his friends hadn't been allowed to pick the daffodils in theirs.

Tom and I decided that the next weekend we would visit Bluebell wood and Daffodil wood to see what they looked like now. Neither of us had seen our woods since we were children, so we didn't know if they'd changed, or if they still looked just the same as they used to look.

The next Saturday we set off. From Tom's house in Farndale we set off walking across the fields. There were lots of other people walking as well. People had come in their cars from miles away to see the beautiful countryside in this part of Yorkshire. We walked down a narrow muddy lane, past two or three tumbledown farm cottages, over a stile and into another field. We followed the path through the grass towards the trees and the stream at the bottom of the field.

And there they were. Thousands and thousands of tiny, wild, yellow daffodils nodding and dancing in the wind. They were growing up the sides of the stream, under the trees, by the hedges, in the grass, everywhere. They were beautiful. Lots of people were walking on our path now, and they were all enjoying the daffodils. No-one was trampling them down or picking them. People would have been angry if anyone had done either of those things.

Tom and I spent a long time with the daffodils in Farndale, and then we walked back to Tom's house and the car, to set off to find Bluebell wood, and to see how that looked.

We found it behind the house where I used to live. It was tiny, muddy, and filled with rubbish. The trees were all broken and dead. They had long since had their branches torn down. The bushes had been pulled up and trampled down, and the bluebells, well, they were long gone. Not one was left growing. They had all been picked or trodden into the mud. We went home feeling sad.

Wasn't it a pity that people, including my friends and I, didn't leave all the bluebells to grow and be enjoyed. If we had all left them alone, they would still be giving people pleasure and enjoyment, like the Farndale daffodils.

Prayer

Thank you, God, for the beauty of wild flowers.
Help us to enjoy them by leaving them to grow
    so that they live as long as they can,
    and so that others can enjoy them too.
Help us remember not to pick them or damage them in any way.

Amen

Hymn

'Think of a world without any flowers' **C&P**

Flowers worth more than gold   *Week 1   Flowers*

The hymn says daisies are silver, buttercups are gold, speedwell flowers are sapphires and even raindrops are diamonds, but you might think that's silly. How can flowers be worth as much as jewels?

I could go to the shops and buy a bunch of flowers, but I certainly couldn't afford to buy a bunch of diamonds!

And yet, flowers, like precious jewels, are beautiful; but we can enjoy the beauty of flowers even if we have no money.

There was once a man who had both wealth and flowers, but he chose flowers as the best.

The man was called Bob Mason, and he worked at a dye factory – a place where the colours are made to dye the materials for our clothes.

Mr Mason was in charge of the machines, which regulated the dye liquid into huge vats for the cloth to go in. He was in charge of the chemicals entering the vats. Mr Mason was quite a happy man. He had a good job with good pay. He had a wife and children and friends. He played football in his local team and played darts in the pub team. Everything in his life was fine . . . until one day, when there was an accident at work.

Inside Mr Mason's regulating machine, was a valve, not working. Pressure was building up inside the pipes, but Mr Mason didn't know because a dial was also not working. He had just checked that length of pipe and that dial, and everything seemed normal. Suddenly there was a huge explosion and acid came pouring out of the vat, on to Mr Mason's clothes, hands, face and eyes. His skin, hair and face were badly burned and he couldn't see.

Bob Mason was rushed to hospital where he had an emergency operation. He was in hospital a long time, and slowly his burns healed, but I'm afraid his eyes didn't. At first the doctors thought he would be able to see again, but as time went on, and Mr Mason could still only see white in the daytime and black at night, it became obvious that he was blind.

Slowly and painstakingly, Mr Mason had to learn to do all the things again that he had done without thinking before the accident. He had to learn to walk, to get washed and dressed, to eat and drink, to make a cup of tea; all without being able to see. Bob Mason felt unhappy, helpless and angry.

He was sent home from hospital, to get on with his life as best he could. He was paid a very large amount of money – compensation – by his firm, because the accident had happened and because he couldn't go to work any more. So now, for the first time in his life, Bob Mason was a rich man. He had thousands of pounds; but he wished he had his sight back.

A long time after the accident, Mr Mason went to see his doctor for a check-up, and the doctor said, 'You know, there's an operation you could have, which might help your eyes. It's not guaranteed to work of course; it might work, it might not. Do you want to try it?'

'I'll try anything', answered Bob Mason, 'which might give me back my sight.'

So the arrangements were made, and Mr Mason went into hospital again. He had the operation, and then for eight days he had to wait with bandages over his eyes. He had to wait, not knowing whether the operation had worked: not knowing whether or not he would ever see again.

At last the eighth day came. Nurses came and stood round his bed. One of the nurses gently began to remove the bandages. Slowly, carefully, they were all taken away from his face. Bob Mason sat in his hospital bed facing the window opposite, and very slowly, very cautiously, opened his eyes. He saw . . . yellow. Blurred, moving, yellow shapes danced before his eyes. His face looked puzzled. Then a huge smile spread across it. The blurred, dancing, yellow shapes were daffodils in the hospital garden. Bob Mason could see. At that moment those daffodils were much more precious to Bob than all the money in the world.

When he got home again, Bob Mason started gardening, and he planted hundreds and hundreds of bulbs, because he never wanted to forget the joy of seeing those dancing yellow daffodils outside his hospital window.

So you see, flowers can be very precious, and they are things we can all enjoy, because we can see. Keep your eyes open, and see them, so that their beauty isn't wasted.

Prayer

> Thank you, God, for the joy and pleasure of seeing spring flowers,
>> after a long, cold, dark winter.
>
> Thank you for their sunshine colours.
>
> Help us to realise how valuable flowers are, to our happiness.
>
> *Amen*

Hymn
'Daisies are our silver' **ChP**

Toffee, the golden labrador
Week 2   Animals

How many of you have a pet at home? Yes, I thought there would be a lot of you. We have pets at school of course, as well. We have (*name any school pets, and if possible bring them into assembly*).

If we have a pet, it's our job, our responsibility to care for it properly: to give it the right kind of food, to give it the right kind of exercise and space, to give it a place to sleep, and to care about it.

Today's story is about someone's pet.

Jane saw it first: a beautiful warm, soft bundle of honey-coloured fur, lying on a bed of sawdust in the pet-shop window. She tapped on the glass and the beautiful golden labrador puppy lifted its head and looked straight at her with its dark brown eyes.

'Oooh, it's lovely', said Jane.

'Oh mum, can we buy it?' asked her brother.

'Don't be silly,' said Jane and Darren's mum, 'we didn't come shopping to buy a dog. Come on!'

'Oh, go on mum', pestered Jane.

'Yes, let's have him', nattered Darren; and before they knew what they were doing, they were inside the shop buying the puppy.

'We'll call him Toffee,' decided Jane, 'because he's toffee coloured.'

When they arrived home, Darren realised they hadn't a bed or any food for Toffee. He made a bed out of a cardboard box and an old blanket, while Jane went to the shop for some dog food. For the next few days Jane and Darren spent all their spare time playing with Toffee, and sometimes they forgot that he was only a young puppy, and needed sleep and quiet times as well as play times.

Jane and Darren's dad was not very pleased about having Toffee in the house. He thought dogs were a nuisance, and got cross every time Toffee jumped onto the chairs, or made a wet puddle on the floor. Nobody thought to train Toffee to keep off the furniture, or to housetrain him. Everyone just shouted at him when he did something wrong, but no-one made him understand why they were cross.

One day, Darren and Jane were watching television, and their mum was getting the tea ready. Toffee was restless because no-one had bothered to take him out for a walk, and he was getting in everyone's way.

'Oh mum, he's chewed my reading book', grumbled Jane.

'Get off my shoe', shouted Darren to the puppy.

'Down', screamed their mum from the kitchen. 'Don't you dare scratch that wallpaper.'

The children's father walked in just as Toffee made yet another puddle on the kitchen floor.

'Get out', shouted the children's dad, and he kicked Toffee out of the back door. The puppy yelped in pain as he rolled down the steps, and scrambled to his feet at the bottom. He ran for all he was worth, away from the pain and the shouting voices. He didn't know where he was going, he simply ran on and on until a car hit him and threw him into the gutter at the edge of the road. Toffee lay there in the muddy water, whimpering in pain and fear.

He lay there, quite still, for a long time, his golden coat matted with mud and blood. No-one took any notice of him. He looked as though he was dead.

At last a man noticed him, and gently lifted the puppy up and wrapped him in a jacket. Toffee was taken to the vet, who cleaned him up, stitched his cuts, and put his broken leg into a plaster. The man who had found Toffee, took him home, and he and his wife cared for the puppy until he was well again. No-one from Toffee's other family looked for him, or tried to find him.

In his new home, Toffee was well looked after. The man housetrained him and taught him to sit, stay, come and walk to heel. Toffee was quick to learn. His new owners and Toffee soon became very fond of each other. The new owners tried to find Toffee's first family, but were not able to. They had almost decided that they would keep Toffee, to live with them always, when something happened that made the decision for them.

One night, Toffee's new owners had gone to bed as usual, after putting Toffee in his own bed in the kitchen. Toffee had gone to sleep almost straight away, but then had woken up again, with a strange smell in his nostrils. He felt sure something was wrong, but all was quiet in the house. Then he saw it. Grey smoke was curling under the kitchen door. Toffee leapt out of bed and barked as loudly as he could. He jumped at the door and scratched at it hard with his front claws. He barked and scratched again and again. He *had* to wake up his owners and warn them about the fire.

It worked. Toffee's new people came down the stairs, coughing and choking in the smoke. They came to the kitchen to get Toffee, and escaped through the back door to safety.

Later, the fireman said that if it hadn't been for the puppy waking the people as soon as the fire started, the damage would have been much worse, and everyone might even have died in the fire.

'You've earned your keep', said the new owners to Toffee. 'You can certainly stay and live here always.'

'Woof', said Toffee.

I'm glad Toffee's new owners looked after him properly. The first owners didn't think properly about the responsibilities of having a dog, before they bought Toffee, and it wasn't a good idea to buy a puppy knowing that one of the family didn't like dogs. We should only have pets if we are prepared to give them time, care and love.

Prayer

Thank you, God, for our pets.
Help us to remember that it is our responsibility
        to care for our pets properly.
Help us to treat our pets well, and train them to fit into our families.

Amen

Hymn

'He's got the whole world' **C&P**

The boys and the frogs

adapted from Aesop

Week 2   Animals

In our last assembly we talked about being responsible for our pets; it is our job to take care of the animals that live in our homes. It is also our job, our responsibility, to look after *all* animals. There are hundreds of different kinds of creatures living with us in the world, and they all have a right to live, just as we do. We must care for the wild animals as well as our pets.

One day a group of boys, about the same age as some of you, went out to play on their bikes in the school holiday. Usually they rode their bikes round the estate where they lived, or on the spare ground at the back of the flats, but on this particular day they went further away. They followed a road to the edge of the estate, went on past some factories, through some fields and to the edge of a small wood. Then they stopped for a rest.

'Hey, look over here', shouted one of the boys, 'there's a pond. I didn't know this was here.'

The other boys gathered round, and looked over the small stone wall at the side of the road.

'Let's go down', they shouted. They left their bikes propped against the wall, and scrambled down the small muddy slope to the pond. It was covered in slimy green weed, with just a clear space of water in the middle. They pulled branches down from the trees and poked them into the water to see how deep it was. Then one boy noticed a frog, and another and another swimming about among the weeds. He picked up a stone and threw it at the swimming frogs.

'Frogs!' shouted another boy. 'Let's see how many we can hit. First to hit ten is the winner.'

All the boys threw down their sticks and scrabbled about at the muddy edge of the pond, picking up stones.

'I got one', yelled one of the boys.

The frogs swam around the pond in panic. Some of them tried to hide in the weed, others hopped to the land and tried to hide under stones or in the mud. One of the frogs, larger and braver than the others, poked his head up out of the water, and to the boys astonishment they thought he spoke.

'Stop. And think before you throw any more stones in here. It may be a game to you, but it is life and death for us.'

The boys stood stock still and gazed at each other in amazement. Not one of them spoke, but each one of them felt ashamed, because they *had* treated it as a game. They hadn't really meant to kill the frogs.

'Let's go home, and play by the flats', someone said.

'Good idea, come on.'

The boys climbed muddily back up the slope, climbed on their bikes and rode off.

Each one of them had learned a lesson.

Sometimes, like those boys, we don't realise that we are actually killing animals. There used to be many Natterjack toads living in England, but now there are hardly any because their ponds have been filled in by builders making new houses. I don't suppose the builders realised they were killing the toads by taking away their ponds.

There are many other animals that man is 'accidentally' killing. We must remember the words of the frog in the story 'It may be a game to you, but it's life and death for us', and we must try to protect the wild animals in our world.*

Prayer

> Dear God, help us to be responsible for our pets,
> but help us also to be responsible towards the wild animals of our world.
> Help us to protect wild animals, and to do nothing that will harm them.
>
> *Amen*

Hymn

'I love God's tiny creatures' **SSL**

*Here, I drew the children's attention to the GPO stamps (actually issued 20 May 1986) featuring Nature Conservation Species at Risk. (The postcards are better illustrative material for assembly use: PHQ cards Nos. 92 A–D available at major Post Offices and from The British Philatelic Bureau, 20 Brandon Street, Edinburgh EH3 5TT.)

The four species illustrated, including the Natterjack Toad, represent animals that have gained some security due to an enlightened approach to conservation.

The hedgehog boy   *Week 2   Animals*

There are lots of big organisations which help to look after or protect animals. I'm sure you will have heard of some of them. There's the RSPCA (Royal Society for the Prevention of Cruelty to Animals), which as its name says, helps to stop animal cruelty. There's the RSPB (Royal Society for the Protection of Birds) which has many bird sanctuaries. There's the World Wildlife Fund which aims to protect animals from all over the world. But it isn't just big organisations which are responsible for caring for wildlife; we are all responsible, and must all try to look after wildlife and never do anything to damage it. Sometimes, we can find a way of helping wildlife quite by accident, just like the boy in today's story.

The boy lived with his mum and dad in an ordinary house, with an ordinary garden, in a quite ordinary street. One night just after he had gone to bed, he heard a shuffling, snuffling noise in the garden below his window. He quietly opened the window and looked out. At first he could see nothing, then as his eyes grew used to the dim light outside he saw two shapes, each about the size of a small rugby ball, moving about at the edge of the lawn. The shapes were making grunting, snorting noises.

'They're hedgehogs', said the boy, and he quickly put on his dressing gown and slippers and went downstairs.

'Mum, can I have a saucer of bread and milk for the hedgehogs?' he asked.

'What?' she said, and he told her about the hedgehogs in the garden. Quickly they made a saucer of bread and milk, and quietly they crept outside to the garden.

The boy was surprised that they were able to get so close to the hedgehogs. As soon as the animals heard the footsteps of the boy and his mother, they curled into tight, prickly balls and sat perfectly still. The boy put the saucer of food just a little way from them, and then squat down on the grass and stayed quite still.

After a short while, both hedgehogs uncurled themselves and sniffed the air with their twitchy noses. When they were sure there was no danger, they came forward on short stiff legs to the saucer and noisily guzzled all the bread and milk before running off into the flower bed for more foraging.

The boy was delighted.

'Aren't they lovely?' he said to his mum. 'I've never been as close as that to hedgehogs before.'

The next day he looked at the books in the school library, and with the help of his teacher, found a lot of information about hedgehogs. He decided they were his favourite wild animals because they were gentle and busy. He also decided that every night he would put out a saucer of bread and milk for them.

The weekend after the boy had seen the hedgehogs in his garden, the boy went out in the car to the country, with his mum and dad. They rumbled over a cattle grid in the road, and pulled into a parking space for their picnic. After he had eaten, the boy walked back to the cattle grid, and began walking over the bars, balancing carefully so that he did not fall. He looked down at the space between and below the bars. It was a shallow space, filled with old soil and dead leaves. Then he noticed something else. It was a hedgehog. It must have fallen between the bars of the grid, and now it couldn't get out. The boy carefully lifted the hedgehog out of the cattle grid and gently put it down in the long grass by a fence.

Then he looked again at the space below the cattle grid. He called his dad to come and look, and asked his dad if all cattle grids were the same shape.

'Well, yes, more or less,' said his dad, 'why do you want to know?'

The boy explained about the hedgehog being stuck in the bottom of the grid, unable to get out. 'If the sides were not straight', he said, 'if there was a sort of ramp, the hedgehogs would be able to get out again, and it wouldn't matter if they fell in, because they wouldn't be trapped. We could put a small sloping piece of wood in every cattle grid, and it would save lots of hedgehogs.'

And that is exactly what the boy and his father did. They had to get permission from the farmers of course, and they had to fix small hooks at the top of the pieces of wood, to stop them slipping down into the bottom of the grids, but the hedgehog ramps worked, and that boy's simple idea saved the lives of hundreds of hedgehogs.

Even that quite ordinary boy did something to help wildlife. You may not be able to invent a hedgehog ramp, but you can put food out for birds, or perhaps persuade your mum and dad to plant bushes in your garden to attract birds and insects. You can also make sure that you never hurt any creatures.

Prayer

> Thank you, God, for the work of the World Wildlife Fund,
> the RSPB, the RSPCA, and all the other organisations
> that help animals and wildlife.
> Help us all to play our part, by looking after wildlife
> and never destroying it.
>
> *Amen*

Hymn

'Who put the colours in the rainbow' **C&P**

The duck pond　　　　　*Week 3　Caring for the environment*

Everyone in our school, the children, the teachers, the caretaker, the dinner ladies and even the cook, tries all the time to look after our school building. We do that so that we have a pleasant place to come to each day. It would be miserable if we let our walls fall in, and never mended our broken windows, or if we let litter pile up outside the doors, or if we never put pictures, plants or paintings in our classrooms and corridors. Our school would look so ugly we wouldn't want to come each day.

It's our job to look after our school. In fact it's our job to look after our neighbourhood, and even our whole world, if we want it to be a good place to live in. In today's story, someone didn't do a very good job of looking after their environment.

Mr and Mrs Watson lived in a small house in the middle of a busy city, but they also had a caravan which they kept on a small caravan site a few miles away, in the country. Every Friday night from Spring to Autumn, Mr and Mrs Watson packed their weekend bags, and stayed at their caravan until Sunday night, when they went home again.

They liked their caravan. They liked being out in the country. They liked to hear the birds sing; they liked to see the flowers and trees; but best of all they liked the animals, especially the ones on the way to the duck pond.

There was a long, leafy lane from their caravan site to the duck pond, and on the way down it Mr and Mrs Watson used to stop and talk to the three donkeys and the two goats that lived in the field at the side. All the way down the lane there were daffodils and primroses growing, and at the end of the lane was the pond with bullrushes growing all round it, and six white ducks swimming in the middle of it.

Sometimes the ducks were scrabbling in the long grass at the pond edge for food, but always, when they saw people coming towards them, they quacked and waddled their way over to the people in the hope of bread to eat. Mr and Mrs Watson never disappointed them, they always took bread for the ducks.

Then, last spring, something happened. A family from the city came to the caravan site for the day. They unpacked their picnic near to Mr and Mrs Watson's caravan. They left their bread papers and their crisp bags and their empty cans and bottles strewn all over the grass when they'd finished their picnic. Then they walked down the lane towards the duck pond.

One of the boys in the family picked up a stick and chopped at the daffodils and primroses all the way down the lane. He left a trail of dead flowers behind him. Neither his mum nor his dad said a word! The girl climbed onto the gate of the donkey field and threw stones at the animals until they ran away, frightened, to the farthest corner of the field. When they came to the duck pond, the six white ducks came waddling across as usual, but the family's dog went for them, grabbing one of the ducks by its neck. It fell to the grass, dead. The other ducks flew and ran, squawking across the grass to the pond, and beyond it to the cottage buildings. The boy ran after them, chopping the air with his stick. When he couldn't catch the ducks he slashed at the bullrushes and broke their long slim stems.

By now the family was bored. They didn't seem bothered by the broken flowers or reeds, or by the dead duck, or by the frightened animals. They set off home, back to the city.

This spring when Mr and Mrs Watson visit the duck pond, the flowers in the lane are growing again, but there are notices all down the lane saying, 'Do not pick the flowers', and 'Keep your dog under control', and 'People causing damage to wildlife will be fined', so the lane doesn't look as pretty as it used to. And when Mr and Mrs Watson walk up to the duck pond, there are no ducks waddling to greet them, waiting to be fed; instead, five white ducks run away from any human beings they see.

What a pity that one family of thoughtless, careless people spoiled the enjoyment of the duck pond for everyone else, and how unfair it was that they were cruel to animals who had done nothing to human beings except trust them.

We all have a job to care for and look after all living things, wherever they are.

Prayer

Dear God, please help us to look after the places where we live.
Help us to care for all the wildlife near our homes;
    the plants, insects, birds and animals.
Help us to protect our environment, to look after
    all the places round about us.

Amen

Hymn
'Stand up, clap hands' **SSL**

The factory plans   *Week 3   Caring for the environment*

Caring for our environment means looking after the places round about us.
It means looking after plants and animals so that we don't kill them. It
means keeping places free from litter, like tin cans and plastic bags, which
can kill animals.

It also means thinking ahead for the future so that we protect our countryside. Today's story is about two people who made plans. One of them
tried to care for countryside and wildlife, and the other one didn't. See if
you can tell which is which.

There was a very big company in London, which sold computers and calculators and electronic machines, that grew so big it needed a new factory.
The people in charge of the company had a meeting and decided they must
build the new factory in Yorkshire, in the north of England. They travelled
to Yorkshire, looked around, and chose a large piece of land in the country,
which they thought would be just right to build a new factory on.

'Now, what sort of building shall we have?' they said. They called in their
architects – people who draw plans of new buildings – and said, 'What do
you think our new factory should look like?' but the two architects couldn't
agree. One of them wanted a tall thin building, and the other thought it
should be long and low.

'We'll have a competition', said the managing director. 'You can both
draw plans for the new factory, we will look at them and choose the plan
we like the best. The architect who draws the best plans will have five
thousand pounds as a prize, and his plan will be made into our new factory.'

The two architects went away and began work.

The first architect travelled to Yorkshire to look at the land where the
factory was to be built. There were some large rocks at one side of the land,
a stream at the other side, and some trees in the distance.

'It's nice here', thought the architect. 'I'll plan the factory on that flat
grass next to those rocks. It'll be a long, stone building, with big windows
so that the workers can look out and see blue sky, and the trees and the
stream. I think I'll put some seats near the trees and the stream, then at
lunch time the workers can sit outside and eat their sandwiches. I'll make
sure the building matches the other buildings nearby and then it won't look
odd; and I'll plan a garden all round the factory, with hundreds and hundreds
of flowers in it.'

Having decided how his plans were going to look, the first architect went back to London to draw them, and the second architect travelled to Yorkshire to look at the piece of land.

'Oh dear', said the second architect. 'This is no good. Those rocks will have to go. That stream will have to be filled in, and those trees must be chopped down. First I'll plan to clear everything away, then I'll concrete the whole area. I'll build a huge, high concrete factory. I won't put windows in it. We can't do with workers wasting time looking out of windows. They will be in the factory to work. Those nearby houses will have to be pulled down, they are in the way. I'll plan a huge road round the factory and then deliveries will be able to get in and out easily. Those fields can be made into roads.'

And having decided how his plans were going to look, the second architect went back to London to draw them.

Two weeks later the managing director and all the other important people of the company looked at the plans and chose the one they wanted. It was easy to choose because they all liked the same architect's plans the best. The winning architect was given the five thousand pounds prize and the building was started straight away.

Very soon it was filled with workers, happily making hundreds more computers, calculators, and electronic machines.

But, the story doesn't tell us which architect won the prize. Do you think it was the first one who thought about the workers, and tried to make the factory fit into the countryside, or do you think it was the second, who got rid of the countryside by covering it in concrete?

Prayer

Thank you, God, for the countryside and for all living things.
Help us to care for our world.

Amen

Hymn
'Think of a world without any flowers' **C&P**

The Fire of London   *Week 3   Caring for the environment*

This week we are thinking about looking after the places round about us. We all try to look after our school, our homes and our neighbourhood. If we have any rubbish or litter we put it into our waste bins or dustbins, and the bin men take it away to burn or bury it. But in London, three hundred years ago, the people didn't bother trying to be clean with their rubbish. I'll tell you what happened. It's a true story.

Three hundred years ago, London was a busy bustling city, with lots of people living in it; not as many people as now, but lots, nevertheless. The people lived in tiny wooden houses, all huddled together round streets and yards by the side of the river Thames. In lots of ways the people were like us, but they didn't have dustbins outside their houses, like we have today.

If your mum or dad peels potatoes for your meal, they throw the peelings into the bin, don't they? Three hundred years ago the people simply threw their peelings out into the street.* If you eat an orange, you put your orange peel into the bin, but three hundred years ago the people just threw their peel into the street. They threw all their rubbish and dirt out of their windows into the street. If they had a bowl of dirty water, they would throw that out into the street as well. The people who lived nearest the river used to throw their rubbish and dirt into that instead of the street. Rubbish floated about on the river, the streets were clogged with it. When it rained the rubbish turned into a sodden, soggy mess. When it was dry and sunny the mess smelled awful. Flies buzzed about on it, and insects crawled over it. Rats ran about in it, and germs grew and then spread. Many, many people became ill with a disease called the plague, and hundreds of people died.

You even know a song about it!
'Ring a ring o' roses,
A pocket full of posies,
Atishoo, atishoo,
All fall down.'
The ring o' roses was a rosy red skin disease that people used to get. The pocket full of posies were bunches of sweet smelling herbs that people used to carry to cover up the awful smells and to ward off the germs. 'Atishoos' were the sneezes that people often had before they became seriously ill; and 'all fall down' was what people did when they died.

Soon, almost half the people in the whole of the city of London were dead.

And then the fire started. It swept along through the rubbish, burning everything and everybody in its way. The houses burned to the ground, many with people inside them. The people that could, ran away for their lives. The whole city was in ashes.

Some time later, the people returned and rebuilt the city. The houses were built of bricks and stones instead of wood, and this time, the people tried to be much more careful with their rubbish.

I think it must have been horrible, living with all that rubbish everywhere. We must make sure that nothing like that ever happens again, by keeping the places we live in and visit, clean and tidy. Perhaps today, as you go around our school, you could pick up and put in the bin, any piece of rubbish you find, even if you didn't drop it. I'll begin by cleaning up all this rubbish at the front of the hall.

Prayer

Help us, Lord, to keep our school and home, our gardens and streets,
    and our playgrounds and fields, clean and tidy.
Help us to remember to throw our rubbish away in the proper place.
If there is no rubbish bin, help us to remember
    to take our rubbish home to our dustbins.

Amen

Hymn
'Milk bottle tops and paper bags' **SSL**

As the story progressed, I scattered around me, at the front of the hall, all the items mentioned. I peeled a potato and an orange and scattered the peelings, upended a bin of assorted rubbish, and even, to the horror of the children, threw an inch or so of washing up water onto the floor. The point was clearly brought home to them by these actions. At the end of the assembly, before the children left the hall, I cleared it all up with the help of a few volunteers.

The ivory box
Week 4   Boxes

In our last few assemblies, we have been thinking about caring for things; caring for flowers, caring for animals and caring for our surroundings. I hope you all try to take care of your belongings as well. Today I have a story about something that lots of people took care of. If they hadn't looked after it, there wouldn't have been a story to tell you. The story, by the way, is absolutely true.

One hundred and twenty years ago, a young man went travelling, to see the world. He visited many countries and had lots of adventures. The last country he visited was India, and while he was there, he went shopping to buy presents to take home with him for all the people in his family. He especially wanted to buy a really lovely present for his sister. The man searched in the markets and bazaars. He looked at lots of different things. Then, just as he was coming out of a small, dark shop, he saw the most beautiful ivory box in the world. It was really a sewing box, and had tiny bobbins and tapemeasures, button boxes and pincushions inside it. It was made of creamy-white ivory, decorated with black ebony, and was lined with sweet smelling cedar wood. It locked with a tiny golden key in a fancy, carved keyhole.

'It's perfect', said the young man to himself, 'but I'll have to be very careful taking it home.'

You see, the young man had a great deal of travelling to do, just to get home. He couldn't get on a plane, because there weren't any planes in those days. He had to travel by train and horse and ship. He packed the ivory box very carefully, and looked after it carefully, all the way home.

His sister was delighted with it. 'It's beautiful', she said, 'I'll take very great care of it', and she did. She kept the box in her bedroom, and put her sewing things in it. Soon, the girl, whose name was Martha, got married. She moved to a home of her own, and of course the box went with her. She carefully looked after it in her new home. Martha had five children, and soon had so much sewing to do, that it wouldn't all fit in the ivory box, so she put her sewing in another box, and kept important papers locked in the ivory box.

One day the tiny golden key to the box was lost and Martha had to break the lock to take out the papers inside. On that day she cried because she had damaged the box she had looked after so well. Luckily it was only the lock that was broken, the rest of the beautiful ivory box looked just as lovely as it had always done.

Martha kept on looking after her box until she was an old, old lady, and then she gave it to her daughter, Kathleen.

Kathleen carefully carried the box to her house and put it on her dressing table. She decided to keep her jewelry in the box. She put cotton wool in the bottom of the box, and then put in her watch and her rings, her bracelet and her necklace. Each week when she cleaned her house, she carefully dusted the ivory box and sometimes she polished it until it gleamed and shone.

One day when Kathleen was at the shops, her husband at work, and her little girl at school, a burglar crept round the back of the house. He broke the kitchen window and climbed into the empty house. No-one saw him go in, and no-one saw him come out, carrying Kathleen's ivory box under his arm. The burglar ran to the wood near Kathleen's house. He sat on the grass, opened the box, took out all Kathleen's jewelry and stuffed it into his pockets. Then he threw the beautiful, creamy-coloured, ivory box, that everyone had taken such care of, into the wet bushes.

When Kathleen got home and found that a burglar had been in her house, she was so upset. She told the police and they looked for the burglar, the stolen jewelry and the box.

A few days later, a man was walking his dog in the woods, when he saw something pale and creamy-coloured, lying in the bushes. He picked it up, and saw that it had been a beautiful ivory box, but now it was broken and dirty. The rain had made it wet, its lid was hanging off, and pieces of ivory were broken or missing.

'Oh, dear, what a pity', said the man. 'It must have been a beautiful box, once', and he took it to the police. Two days later it was back in Kathleen's house, but how sad she felt when she saw it. All the years that people had taken care of it, now seemed wasted. It was very badly damaged.

Kathleen searched and searched for someone who could repair the ivory box, but everyone said, 'Oh no! I can't do anything with that. It's damaged beyond repair.' And then she found a man working in an old tumble-down cottage. 'Mmm', he said. 'I think with care I can do something with it.'

Carefully and slowly he worked. Slowly and carefully. Each day gluing, damping, hammering, polishing. At last the ivory box was as good as new. Kathleen was so pleased to have it back.

Today the box is back on her dressing table, and every day she carefully dusts it. Perhaps one day Kathleen will give it to her daughter, who, I am sure, will look after it as carefully as all the other people did, except of course the burglar, who should have known better.

The ivory box is on Kathleen's dressing table today because people took care of it. If we care for our things, then they might last a long time, and give us pleasure for a long time.

Prayer

> Dear God, thank you for our toys and books,
> and presents that people have given us.
> Please help us to look after our things and to take care of them.
> Please help us to care for other people's belongings as well as our own,
> and never to damage anything on purpose.

Amen

Hymn
'Thank you Lord' **C&P**

The treasure box

People put all kinds of things into boxes. I expect you have boxes for things at home. You'll probably have a toy box, your mum or dad might have a tool box, you might have a blanket box. You'll probably have smaller boxes as well, a biscuit box, and a box for sweets or chocolates. Your teachers keep things in boxes in your classrooms. There are dressing up boxes and boxes for workcards. Almost anything can be put into a box.

Our story today is about someone who put something into a box.

There was once a poor tailor who made very good suits, jackets, trousers and coats. He made such good clothes that the King heard about them, and asked the tailor to make him a coat. The tailor worked and worked in his tiny, dark workroom. He cut beautiful cloth and sewed fine stitches with silk thread. He stitched on gold and silver buttons, and a collar of velvet. At last the coat was finished and the tailor took it to the palace.

The King tried the coat on, and twizzled and turned in front of his mirror to see what he looked like in it. At last he stood still and said, 'It's a very fine coat. In fact, it's the finest I've seen. You're an excellent tailor. You can be my Royal tailor from now on.'

'Oh thank you', said the tailor.

From that very day, the tailor went to the King's palace every week to show the King materials and to sew the King's new clothes.

The King soon learned that the tailor was very good at something else besides sewing. He was very good at listening and giving advice. Sometimes the King would tell the tailor about some problem or other, and the tailor would listen carefully, and then he would suggest to the King that he try this, or that, or the other, to solve the problem. The tailor was a very kind, fair, thoughtful man, and he always gave the King good advice.

One day, as he was trying on a new suit, the King said, 'I think you are too clever to be my tailor. I would like you to come and live at the palace and be my Prime-Minister-and-Chief-Adviser. What do you say?'

The tailor stood still and thought.

'Yes,' he said, 'I would like to do that.'

'Good,' answered the King, 'you can start tomorrow.'

The very next day the tailor packed all his things, and moved to his new home in the King's palace, ready to start his new job.

The tailor became a very good Prime-Minister-and-Chief-Adviser, and helped lots of important people in the palace, as well as the King, but the people in the palace noticed something very strange about him. Wherever he went, the Prime-Minister-and-Chief-Adviser always carried with him a small wooden box. The people said, 'What is it he keeps in his box? He takes it everywhere with him.'

'It must be something so valuable, he dare not put it down or leave it anywhere', they said.

'It must be treasure', they said.

'Perhaps it is treasure that belongs to the King', they said.

'Perhaps it is treasure he has stolen from the King', they said.

'That's it!' the people shouted. 'He is stealing jewels from the King's treasure house, and he is hiding them in that wooden box. He never puts it down or leaves it anywhere, because he doesn't want anyone to look inside and know that he is stealing the King's jewels.'

The people decided to take the Prime-Minister-and-Chief-Adviser to the King, and make him open the wooden box, and show the King the stolen jewels. They caught hold of him and marched him to the King. Then they explained to the King about the stolen jewels they thought were in the box.

'Well?' said the King. 'Is there treasure in that wooden box of yours?'

'Yes,' answered the Prime-Minister-and-Chief-Adviser, 'I'll show you.' He opened the box, and there inside were pins and needles, scissors and thread, the tailor's chalk – all the tools that a tailor uses. 'This is my treasure', he said. 'I keep my tailor's tools in this box to remind me of my humble beginnings. Now that I have an important job, I might get big-headed, so I keep these things with me to stop me getting big-headed and to remind myself that I am just an ordinary tailor. I have stolen nothing.'

'I am sorry I doubted you', said the King.

'We are sorry', said the people.

'That's all right', said the Prime-Minister-and-Chief-Adviser, 'it doesn't matter.' And he forgave them all for thinking badly of him.

Treasure can be different things to different people. The tailor's tools were treasure to him, and valuable to him because they reminded him of his life as a tailor, before he became important. Perhaps you have something at home that is 'treasure' to you.*

Prayer

> Thank you, God, for all our treasures.
> Help us to realise that things don't have to be worth a lot of money
>> to be treasures to us, to be worth a lot to us,
>> and to mean a lot to us.
> Help us to care for our treasures so that they will give us happiness,
>> for a long time.

Amen

Hymn
'The best gift' **C&P**

At this point, I showed the children various objects that were 'treasures' and 'of value' to various members of staff. These personal treasures ranged from teddy bears to candlesticks. The children were told briefly why each object was valuable to its owner. The children of course were most interested to hear about these personal objects belonging to teachers, and the objects themselves showed beyond any doubt, that things last if they are taken care of.

Pandora's box

I think the best box of all is a surprise box; a box that you don't know what's inside. Of course, if it is a surprise box, you may not like what's inside. Surprises can be awful, as well as good. The box in today's story had a surprise in it.

Many, many years ago, at the beginning of time, when the world was a happy place with no sadness, or selfishness or disease, there lived a beautiful princess called Princess Pandora. Pandora was to be married to the King of a far away kingdom, and everyone brought her presents before she left for the wedding. She was given silver knives and golden forks, plates of crystal and diamond encrusted cups. She was given silken sheets and fine feather pillows, and a beautiful, wonderful, blue glass box. The person who gave her the box said it was just an ornament, and she must never, ever, on any account, even think of opening the box. It must stay shut. Pandora put the box with her other wedding presents.

Soon it was time for Pandora to travel to the King's palace for her wedding. All her presents were packed into the carriage. Pandora climbed in, and put the beautiful, blue, glass box that she must never open, on her knees. The coachman called to the horses, and the carriage set off. Over the roads, up the hills and down the dales they went. The carriage rumbled and jumbled and joggled, and the beautiful, blue, glass box that she must never open, jiggled about on Pandora's knee. Suddenly, the carriage jolted over a stone, the door flew open, and the beautiful, blue, glass box fell out. Luckily it fell into a deep puddle and so it did not break. The coach stopped and Pandora stepped out to pick up the box. As she did so, a voice from nowhere said, 'Leave the box alone, it'll bring you trouble.' 'Trouble', whispered an echo. But Pandora took no notice. She wanted her beautiful, blue, glass box, that she must never open, back again. She picked it up out of the puddle and climbed back into the carriage which then set off again.

Pandora looked at the blue glass box on her knee.

'I wonder what is inside the box', she said to herself. 'I wonder why I can't open it.'

She touched the smooth, shiny, glass lid of the box. She fiddled with the tiny glass key.

'It can't do any harm to have just one little peep inside', she thought. 'I'll turn the key, open the lid a little way, and have a peep. Then I'll close it again. No-one will ever know that I've looked inside.'

Pandora knew that she should not open the box. She knew that she had been told to keep it closed, but she wanted so much, to see what was inside. Very gently, she turned the tiny glass key. Very slowly she began to open the beautiful, blue, glass lid.

'It won't matter', she whispered to herself.

Suddenly the lid snapped open with a bang. There was a flurry and a flutter and hundreds of thousands of tiny, winged insects flew out of the box. Their wings glistened and gleamed as they beat against Pandora's head and arms. Their stings hurt her face and hands. Their brown and black hairy bodies flew in front of her eyes. Pandora cried as she banged the lid shut, and opened the carriage window to let out the dreadful insects. They flew in a cloud to the sky, taking illness, disease and unhappiness to the people of the world.

Pandora heard a tiny voice coming from the now closed box.

'Let me out', it said.

Pandora opened the box again and out flew a beautiful butterfly with jewel-coloured wings. 'My name is Hope,' it said, 'let me out and I will fly after all the evil insects. I cannot undo their evil but I can give people hope of better things.'

Pandora set free the butterfly of hope. She knew she had been wrong to open the box and let out all the insects of evil, but she was glad she had freed Hope.

When everything goes wrong for us, we must remember to hope that things will get better. Hope is always there, fighting troubles.

Prayer
> Thank you, God, for hope.
> Help us to remember not to give up hope when things go wrong.
> Thank you for giving us hope that all our tomorrows
> > will be bright and happy.

Amen

Hymn
'Peace perfect peace' **C&P**

How family names started

What's my name? Put your hand up if you have a name! Put your hand up if you're called Sarah . . . , James . . . , Simon. Everyone has a name. If we didn't have a name no-one would know what to call us. We wouldn't be able to make people understand who we are talking about, if our friends didn't have names. Your teacher wouldn't know whose books belong to who, if they didn't have your names on the front.

Once upon a time hundreds of years ago, there lived a villageful of people, high up in the mountains of a country called Montania. They were happy people; kind, helpful and hardworking. Most of the families had tiny farms, with sheep and goats and cows. The people lived in wooden houses with tall, steep, red roofs, and all the houses had gardens and window boxes full of red, pink, purple, blue and white flowers. It was a good place to live. Or at least, it was a good place to live until the ill wind blew.

The people of Montania had never felt a wind like this one. They were used to the cold, snowy, blowy winds of the mountains in winter, and they were used to the warm, gentle, flower-scented breeze of the mountains in summer; but this wind was a rustling, bustling, busy, hissing sort of wind that ruffled you up and made you feel disagreeable and uncomfortable and restless. From the day the ill wind started, things began to go wrong. Cows stopped giving milk, two sheep died, three goats ran amok in the mountains and fell from a cliff. Vegetables didn't grow, a haystack caught fire, people felt poorly.

Then people noticed something even more strange about the ill wind. It seemed to be whispering people's names.

'Chris–toph–er', it seemed to whistle.

'Steph – Steph – Steph – Stephanie', it whispered.

'Su – san', it hissed.

'It knows some of our names', said the worried people, 'what will we do?'

The people of the village all had a meeting and decided that in future they would never, ever, say people's names out loud, and then the ill wind wouldn't find out the rest of the names. They decided that no-one must call anyone by their name, or even write the name down, in case the ill wind could read.

Well, you can imagine how difficult everything became. Mothers couldn't call their children in for tea, because they were not to speak their names; farmers couldn't call across the fields to tell a worker what to do; shepherds couldn't call across the mountains to each other any more, and nobody knew who anybody was talking about, because no-one could say anyone's name.

'This is no good,' all the people said, 'we'll have to think of a better plan.'

'I know,' said someone, 'we'll give everyone a new name. The ill wind won't know their real name and so it will be all right.'

So all the people chose new names for each other. They decided to give each family a name, so that the wind still wouldn't know which person was which. They called John and his family 'Mountain', because their house was highest on the mountain. They called Sarah and her family 'Roads', because their house was where three roads joined. They called Peter and his family 'Smith', because Peter was the blacksmith. They called Emma and her family 'Waterhouse', because their home was by the stream. The new system worked very well, and the ill wind didn't seem to notice the new names.

One day in early spring, the ill wind did the strangest thing. It blew up all the dust it could find and twirled it high into the sky. Then it swirled the dust round the mountain top and vanished into the distance, never to be seen again. The ill wind was gone.

'Thank goodness for that', said everyone, 'now perhaps everything will start to go right again.' And it did.

'Now we can have our old names back again,' someone said.

'Oh no, we'll keep both our names', said someone else, 'we're used to our new names now. Let's put both our names together.' So for the first time ever, people had a first name and a family name.

'We like our names', said John Mountain, Sarah Roads, Peter Smith and Emma Waterhouse.

We are like the people from Montania because we have a first name and a family name. Perhaps you could find out if *your* family name has a meaning, like the family names in the story.

Prayer

Thank you, God, for our names.

Help us not to call people by silly or unkind names.

Help us to say people's names properly, because names are important.

Amen

Hymn
'The family of man' **C&P**

Finding the name

Week 5   Names

Not only people have names, but things have names as well. Everything around us has a name. Some of those names are easy, and everyone knows them. You all know that this is a table, and that is a piano, over there is a door, and here is a window. But there are some things you might not know the name of. Here is a vase of flowers. You all know that they are flowers, but each flower is different, and each has a name. This yellow one is called Oxford Ragwort, and this white one is called Hedge Parsley.*

Today's story is about a girl who didn't think that names were important.

Jane was having a day out with her dad. He had taken her to a café for lunch and now they were going to the park. Jane's dad was trying to teach her the names of all the different trees.

'That one with the leaves like big fingers, is a horse chestnut', he said, 'and the old gnarled one over there, with the twisted trunk, is an oak.'

But Jane wasn't interested. 'They're just trees,' she said, 'I don't need to know their names.'

Later, her dad tried to teach Jane the names of some wild flowers, but she wasn't listening. 'They're just flowers,' Jane grumbled, 'I don't need to know their names.'

'But you can't find out anything about them, if you don't know their names', said her dad.

'I don't want to find out about them,' argued Jane, 'I want to go home now.' So home they went.

Jane's dad went into the garden to finish digging the new flower bed. 'I'm bored', said Jane as she kicked at the newly turned earth. Suddenly she saw something round and greeny-black in the soil. 'Dad,' she called, 'look. It's a coin.' Her dad came over to look. 'It's just an old coin,' he said, 'it's no good.'

Jane turned the coin over in her hands. She felt its thin, worn edges and its thick raised centre. She felt and saw the shape of a man's head on the back of the coin. She felt how very old it was, and she wondered about its story: when and where was it made, how old was it, what had it bought, why was it in her garden? Her head surged with questions about the coin.

She started to ask her dad.

'Oh, I don't know, Jane,' he said, 'I don't know anything about coins. I think you'll have to begin by finding out who that man is on the coin. When you know his name, you'll be able to find out the name of the coin, and once you've identified the coin, well, you'll be able to find out lots about it from books, and perhaps from the museum.'

Jane looked at her dad in a puzzled way. 'That's what you were saying earlier, isn't it; that to find out about something, you first have to find out exactly what its name is?'

'Yes, that's right', answered her dad.

'Now I understand', said Jane. She went back into the house and looked up 'coins' in her encyclopaedia. The next day at school she asked her teacher about the coin, and found some books in the school library about old coins. By now she had discovered it was a Roman coin. Soon she knew it was a Roman Julius Caesar silver denarius. Now that she knew the name of the coin she was on a treasure trail of discovery. Her mum helped her find out about people's lives in Roman times. Her gran bought her a book about Roman coins; and there was her coin on page 14. But the best discovery was when Jane's mum took her to the museum to ask if they had any information about the silver denarius.

'It's a good one', said the man. 'It's in very good condition. It'll be worth a few pounds if you sell it.

'Oh, I don't want to sell it', answered Jane. 'I want you to put it in your museum where everyone can see it.'

'That's a lovely idea', said the man. 'We'll put it with our other coins and put a label with it saying "donated by Jane Brown".' And he did.

I wonder what you would have done if the coin had been yours.

Prayer

Dear God, thank you for all the exciting things there are in the world.

Help us to remember that if we find out the name of something,
    we have opened a door to discovery.

Help us to want to find out so that we can understand our world better.

Amen

Hymn

'He's got the whole world' **C&P**

*These were the flowers that I used, but a small jar of any wild flowers could be used equally well, providing the children are unlikely to know their names, prior to being told. The aim is to make it clear that there are sub-species, within the main known species.

The Grace Darling   *Week 5   Names*

Everything has a name. Sometimes people give names to their cars or their houses. Your house probably has a number, and it may have a name as well. Your family might have a name for your car. Fishermen usually have names for their boats, and the names are painted on the sides, for everyone to see.

A boy I know once went on holiday to Filey. He walked one day down to the Coble Landing, a place where all the fishing boats are kept when they're being repaired, or when they are waiting to go out to sea. He watched the fishermen mending the nets, loading the lobster pots and cleaning the boats. He looked at the colours the boats were painted; bright blues, reds, greens and yellows. He saw the big wheels and axles that were used to wheel the shallow-bottomed boats down the landing, across the sands and into the sea. He stood by one boat and smelled its fishy, oily smell. He saw writing and numbers on its side.

He pointed to the writing. 'What's it for?' he asked the nearest fisherman.

'The number is her registration number, lad, and the other's her name', said the fisherman.

'The Grace Darling', read the boy. 'Why?' he said.

'Because the boat's named after Grace Darling. She was brave, and the boat carries her name so that it may be brave as well. I'll tell you her story', went on the man.

'Grace was a small girl; lived with her dad in the lighthouse at the Farne Islands, a hundred miles north of here. The Farne Islands are treacherous rocks and the light had to be kept burning to warn fishing boats away. One night there was a terrible storm. Pitch black it was, wind lashing rain down and waves as high as houses. No boat could survive a storm such as that one. Grace Darling and her father kept the light burning in case any ship was at sea. And they saw one. A small fishing coble with about nine half-drowned seamen on board. It didn't have a chance. The waves were tossing it like a bit of rubbish on the sea. Grace's father was for leaving it.

"Can't do anything to help", he said. "We'll be drowned as well, if we go out into that sea!"

'But Grace wouldn't have it. "We can't leave them and watch them drown", she said, "we've got to go out and try to save them."

'Her father said no and she said yes, and in the end she persuaded him. She said the two of them together could manage even in that savage sea. She said they had to try to save the men. Even if they couldn't rescue them, they had at least to try.

'So out they went in their own small boat. Soaking wet in two minutes, they were, but they pressed on. Had to hang on for dear life, or they'd have been thrown out of their own boat and surely drowned. They tossed nearer and nearer to the fishing coble, and by some miracle managed to get five men aboard. Back to the lighthouse they went, then out into the black, heaving sea again. By all accounts they should have capsized, but no, they stayed afloat and brought in the other four men.

'Nine lives saved because of one brave girl who risked her own life to rescue theirs.

'So you see lad, it's a brave name this little boat has to live up to. "The Grace Darling".'

'Thank you for telling me the story', said the boy. 'Is it a true story?'

'Aye lad, it is that', said the fisherman.

Now, whenever the name of Grace Darling is said, everyone remembers her for being brave and for rescuing the fishermen. Let us try to make sure that whenever anyone says our name, they think of something good about us.

Prayer

Thank you, God, for brave people like Grace Darling.
Whenever her name is said, people remember that she was good,
    caring and brave.
Help us to be good and caring and brave as well,
    so that when people say our names they will think well of us.
Help us never to do anything which will make people think badly of us.

Amen

Hymn

'Give me oil in my lamp' **C&P**

The hawk and his friends

Week 6   Friendship

adapted from the Mahāukkusa-Jātaka

The other day I saw two children in our school looking very unhappy. Now that was most unusual because those two children are normally bright and cheerful and the best of friends. When I asked them what was the matter they said they'd fallen out and they didn't care because they didn't need a friend any more. I knew that wasn't true; they did care and everybody needs a friend. We talked about it and I'm pleased to say that by the next playtime they were the best of friends again.

That conversation reminded me of a story about a hawk who once needed some friends.

Once upon a time a hawk asked a she-hawk to be his wife. She said she would, on condition that he had some friends who would help defend them if danger or trouble threatened.

'Oh dear!' said the hawk. 'I don't have any friends and I don't know anyone I can ask to be my friend.'

'Why don't you ask the eagle and the lion, who live at the edge of the lake, and the tortoise who lives on the island in the middle of the lake, to be your friends?' suggested the she-hawk.

The hawk went to ask those animals if they would be his friends and if they would help him if ever he was in trouble.

'Yes,' they each said, 'because that's what friends are for.'

When the hawk had made friends with the animals he married the she-hawk and they settled down to live in a Kadamba tree at the edge of the lake. Soon the she-hawk laid two eggs and a little later the eggs hatched into two fine baby hawks.

One day some hunters came to the lakeside. They hadn't caught any animals during the day so they settled for the night under the Kadamba tree where the hawk family lived. The men lit a fire but the smoke rose into the branches and made the baby birds cough.

'Birds!' shouted the men. 'We'll have them for supper. Kill them!' One man built up the fire whilst another climbed the tree to catch the hawks.

'Quickly,' said the she-hawk, 'get help'. The hawk flew as fast as the wind to the eagle to ask for help. In no time the eagle swooped on the Kadamba tree, knocking the man from its branches. The eagle dived again and again stopping the men from climbing the tree and robbing the nest of the babies. But the eagle was tiring fast. Each dive at the men exhausted him, and he took longer and longer to regain his strength for the next attack.

'Go and ask the tortoise for help', ordered the she-hawk. The hawk set off again and flew to the island in the middle of the lake. The tortoise came immediately. Usually so slow on land, she swam quickly through the water. As she reached the water's edge she gathered up mud in her mouth and spat it onto the hunters' fire to put out the flames.

'Kill the tortoise', shouted the hunters. 'Tortoise meat is tasty. It'll be better than roasted hawk for our supper.'

The men grabbed the tortoise and tried to turn her on her back so that they could kill her, but the tortoise was strong and pulled the men into the lake. They grappled and fought in the swirling muddy water.

'Go and ask the lion for help', shouted the she-hawk. Again the hawk flew off as fast as the wind and in no time a growling, galloping lion was bearing down on the wet hunters in the water.

'First a diving eagle, then a grappling tortoise, now a man-eating lion', they muttered as they took to their heels and ran away as fast as their legs would carry them.

'Thank you friends', said the hawk. 'Thank you for saving my family.'

'Friendship is valuable', answered the lion. 'We must never break our friendship and then we will all be strong.'

And from then on, all the friends lived happily together near the Kadamba tree by the lake, and they always helped each other when help was needed.

The hawk found out that everyone needs friends at some time. It's good to have friends, but to *have* a friend you need to *be* a friend, ready to help when you're needed.

Prayer

Dear God, please help us to be a good friend.

Help us to make friends again if we fall out or quarrel.

Amen

Hymn
'Think, think on these things' **SSL**

Making friends, breaking friends   *Week 6   Friendship*

I have been trying to make a paper chain of dolls, but so far I haven't done very well. I'll try again.*

Friendship is like the joined hands. When hands are joined, it usually means friendship, fun and games.

When hands are not joined, it usually means broken friendships, and broken friends are like the separate dolls in the chain; they are alone and lonely.

We can make friends by using our hands in a friendly way. Can you think of ways hands can be used to be friendly?

Suggestions might be helping hands: carrying things, putting things away; shaking hands to show friendliness; playing games: skipping, ball games; beckoning and welcoming people to our games.

Or, we can break friendships by using our hands in an unfriendly way. Can you think of unfriendly ways hands can be used?

Suggestions might be fighting; hitting and smacking; scratching; pushing.

All these are unkind things to do and will make us lose our friends.

If we are kind and friendly to other people, the chances are they will be kind and friendly to us. When we have friends and when we are together, like the joined paper chain of dolls, we are strong and can do all kinds of things, just because we are together.

There was once a father who told his three sons to be friends and to work together; but the three sons were always arguing and falling out, and never managed to do anything together. One day the father gave each boy a stick.

'Those sticks are like you,' he said, 'they are separate and individual and are easily broken. Look!' and he took each stick in turn and broke it in two.

Then he gave each of the boys another stick, and told them to put the three sticks together in a bundle, and tie the bundle with string. The boys thought this was a strange thing for their father to ask them to do, but they did as they were told and tied their sticks together in a bundle.

'Now watch', said their father. He took the bundle of sticks from them and tried to break it in half. No matter how hard he tried, he could not break the bundle of sticks. It was too strong, because the sticks were fastened together and each was strengthening the other.

'Perhaps now you understand', said the father. 'If you work together in unity, like the bundle of sticks, you will be strong. If you stand alone, like a single stick, you will be broken more easily.'

The boys understood, and tried much harder to be friends and to work together.

The boys at the end of the story were like the paper chain of dolls; friendly and together. I think they were probably happier, too.

Prayer

Thank you, God, for all our friends.
Help us to be thoughtful, kind and helpful to our friends,
and to work together in friendship.

Amen

Hymn
'Look out for loneliness' **SSL**

I prepared two concertina folds of paper, with a doll outline pencilled on the front of each. On the first shape, I deliberately and exaggeratedly cut through the folds so that when the concertina was opened out, the paper dolls scattered to the floor, emphasising the separateness of each. The children were able to suggest where I had made the cutting mistake, and I 'tried again' with the second folded paper. This time, of course, the chain was successful and opened out to reveal dolls holding hands, thus showing unity and friendship.

Opposites attract   *Week 6   Friendship*

Sometimes I like to watch comedy programmes on television, and one of my favourites is Laurel and Hardy. Perhaps you have seen it. It's about two men who are friends, but they are very different from each other. One of them is small and thin, and the other is tall and fat. They seem an unlikely pair to be such good friends. It is strange, but sometimes people who are very different from each other, make extremely good friends. It is not just different people who make friends either; there are some very different animals who have made unlikely friendships as well.

There was once an explorer who was travelling round the world, gathering information about animals, so that he could write a book about animal behaviour. When he arrived in Australia, a group of scientists asked the explorer if he would like to go deep sea diving with them, and of course the explorer said yes. The men set out in a boat carrying all their equipment, and when they had sailed out to the coral reef, they put on their wet suits and their oxygen bottles and masks, and jumped into the water. Down they swam, past the rocks and coral formations, to the pink, coral-studded sea bed.

The explorer was examining a group of spiny sea urchins, when he noticed a large dark shape swimming towards him. It was a shark. The explorer stayed quite still, and watched. The shark was taking no notice of him or the other divers, but was busy catching and eating small fish. The explorer noticed that some small fish were swimming round the shark's head, and even swimming in and out of its mouth, but the shark wasn't eating those fish. The explorer wondered why.

He carried on watching. Then to his surprise, he saw why the shark wasn't eating the small fish that swam around its head. They were cleaning the shark's skin. They were eating all the bits of dirt and debris that were fastened to the shark's skin. They were helping the shark, and it was helping them by not eating them and by protecting them from other fish. What a strange and useful friendship, thought the explorer.

He did not think there would be other animal friendships as strange as that of the shark and the cleaner fish, but he was wrong! A few weeks later, the explorer was visiting New Zealand. He was taken out into the bushland to see how lizards live. Once again, he became quite still so that he could watch the animals without alarming them. Lizards scuttled this way and that on the hot, sandy ground. The explorer noticed a large lizard about half a metre long, disappear into a shallow burrow. No sooner had it vanished into the ground, than a blue-coloured bird flew in after it. The explorer was astonished and expected the lizard to kill and eat the bird, but less than two minutes later, both lizard and bird came out of the burrow, completely unharmed. He asked the people he was with, about the bird and the lizard.

'Oh yes,' they said, 'the birds are called petrels and are the best of friends with the lizards. You see they both lay their eggs in burrows in the ground, so to save making a burrow each, they share each others'. It's a very good arrangement.'

The explorer began to realise that there are lots of unusual animal friendships. Just because animals are different, it doesn't mean that they can't help each other.

We can be like those friendly animals. People don't have to be the same as each other to be good friends. It doesn't matter if people are a different colour, or have different customs, or eat different foods, or live a different lifestyle; they can still be friends and help each other.

Prayer

Help us, Lord, to be helpful and friendly.
Teach us to help our neighbour regardless of:
the colour of his skin
or the place he worships in,
or the place from where he came,
or his unusual name.
Help us to make this a friendly world.

Amen

Hymn
'When I needed a neighbour' **C&P**

Mrs Pink and Mrs Grey   *Week 7   Colours*

I wonder what you would say if I asked you what your favourite colour is. I think lots of you would say different colours. I have brought a box of crayons into assembly today, and I am going to ask the youngest children in school to tell me the names of the colours.

I wonder if the older children can tell me what colours we would have if we mixed some colours together? What would we have if we mixed black and white, red and yellow; blue and yellow; green and blue?

We are lucky that we can see so many different colours, and that we live in a world full of colours.

Sometimes people make me think of colours. I have two neighbours. One of them is called Mrs Wilby. She lives in her house with Mr Wilby. She has a lovely home and a beautiful garden, but I'm afraid Mrs Wilby never really looks happy, and every time she speaks she complains about something.

If I see her in the garden, I say 'Good morning' or 'Hello', as cheerfully as I can. But Mrs Wilby never says a cheerful 'Good morning' back. She says 'Oh dear, isn't it dull and cold today', or 'I wanted to put my washing out today but it looks like rain', or 'I don't feel well today, everything's such an effort, oh dear.'

The silly thing is that Mrs Wilby has nothing to be miserable about. She isn't old, or lonely, or ill. She isn't very poor. She has grown-up children who often come to see her, and she has lovely grandchildren who also often come to see her. She should be very happy, instead of miserable and complaining.

Mrs Wilby reminds me of a colour. I always think of grey when I see her, because grey is a rather dismal, dreary colour.

Now my other neighbour, Mrs Robinson, always makes me think of warm pink and orange colours. She is not at all like grey Mrs Wilby. Mrs Robinson is cheerful and happy. She always has a kind word for everyone, and will say 'Good morning' in a cheery voice, to anyone she meets. Even if it is a gloomy day, Mrs Robinson will find something good about it, to remark on. She is a very busy lady, and is always rushing about helping people. Everyone likes her because she is so helpful and friendly and cheerful.

The funny thing is, she doesn't seem to have all that much to be happy about. Her husband died a long time ago, and she lives all on her own. She hasn't any children or grandchildren; in fact I don't think she has any family at all. She has arthritis which makes her hands and knees very painful, and she has to go to the doctor's and to the hospital quite often. Yet she is always cheerful, and she makes other people feel cheerful as well. It's no wonder that I always think of warm pink and orange colours when I think of her.

Let us try to be cheerful, so that people think of cheerful colours when they see us. Let's make people think of warm sunshine colours when they think of us.

Prayer

Thank you, God, for all the lovely colours around us.
Help us to notice the colours in everything and not to be blind to them.
Help us to be cheerful people so that people think of cheerful,
> warm, sunshine colours when they see us.

Amen

Hymn

'Who put the colours in the rainbow' **C&P**

Princess Midas

I think everyone has a favourite colour: one colour they like better than all the other colours. Sometimes people have favourite colours for different things. Someone might have blue as their favourite colour for clothes, but green as their favourite colour for their bedroom. Or somebody might have red as their favourite colour for shoes, but yellow as their favourite colour for painting on pictures.

Today's story is about someone who had one favourite colour for everything.

You have probably heard the story of King Midas; a king who was so greedy he wanted everything to be turned into gold. When everything *was* turned into gold, he thought he was happy, until his own daughter turned into gold as well. The King was so sorry for being greedy that the magic changed the princess back to herself again, but the story doesn't say that the magic went wrong! The Princess, who had been kind and polite before, turned into a selfish greedy girl.

One day, Princess Midas said to her mother, the Queen, 'My favourite colour is yellow. I want my bedroom to be yellow.'

'Very well dear,' said the Queen, 'we'll arrange to have new yellow wallpaper and carpets and curtains and bedspreads.' By the following week everything in Princess Midas' bedroom was yellow: even the glass in the windows, which made everything outside look yellow.

The next day Princess Midas said, 'I want all my clothes to be yellow. I don't want my red dress or my blue shoes any more. Give me new yellow clothes.'

'Very well dear,' said her father the King, 'you can have as many new clothes as you want and they can all be yellow.' The royal servants went out to the shops and bought yellow dresses and coats, yellow hats and scarves, shoes and socks, yellow vests and nightdresses and even yellow hair-ribbons and yellow slippers. The Princess tried on all the clothes and smiled.

The next day Princess Midas said, 'I want everything in the palace to be yellow.'

'Oh, I don't think that's a very good idea', said her mother the Queen, remembering when the King had turned everything into yellow gold.

'But I want it', shouted the Princess.

'Very well dear', said the Queen and she called in all the palace workmen to change everything to yellow. They set to work and soon everything you could think of in the entire palace was bright yellow.

The next day Princess Midas said, 'I want everything in the royal gardens to be yellow.'

'Oh, I don't think we can do that', smiled her father the King, remembering how silly he had been when he turned everything to yellow gold.

'But I want it', screamed the princess.

'Very well dear', said the King, and he called for the royal gardeners. They worked very hard. They pulled out all the pink, blue, white, orange and red flowers, and planted yellow ones. They put awful-smelling chemicals down to turn the lawns yellow, and they sprayed all the bushes and trees yellow. The gardens looked dreadful, but Princess Midas smiled. 'Now I want everything in the world to be yellow', she said.

'I can't do that', said the King. 'I am not powerful enough to turn everything yellow.'

'But I want it', screamed the princess and she stamped her feet in temper.

Suddenly there was a flash of yellow light, a streak of yellow lightning, and a puffing cloud of yellow smoke. When the smoke cleared, no-one could believe their eyes! Everything, absolutely everything, was vivid, bright yellow. Princess Midas' hair, the King's face, the Queen's skin, the people's hands, the food on the tables, the water in the tap, the clouds, the sky, the air, the soil; everything was yellow.

'I don't like it,' shouted Princess Midas, 'take it away.' But nobody knew how the yellow had happened and so nobody knew how to take it away. Princess Midas, just like her father before her, realised how silly she had been. She understood that too much of anything, even nice things, can be dreadful. As soon as she began to feel truly sorry, the yellow began to fade, and her greedy selfishness began to fade with it.

After one week most things were back to their normal colours. After two weeks the palace workmen had changed everything in the palace back to how it was. After three weeks, everything was back to normal, all except for Princess Midas' hair, which stayed yellow for the rest of her life, just as a reminder to her and the King that you can have too much of a good thing.

It is good to have a favourite colour, but it would be very boring if that colour was everywhere. We need all the different colours to make our lives rich.

Prayer

Dear God, thank you for our colourful world.
Thank you for colours dark and light, pale and deep.
Thank you for all the hundreds of different shades.
Thank you for our eyes to see them with.

Hymn

'He made me' **C&P**

Noah's rainbow
adapted from the Bible

Sometimes, if the weather is sunny, and then it starts to rain while the sun is still shining, something magical appears in the sky; do you know what it is? Yes, it's a rainbow, a beautiful arch of shining colour painted into the sky; red, orange, yellow, green and blue; indigo and violet too; seven shimmering colours high in the sky. There are all sorts of magical stories about rainbows, but the most famous one of all, is the story from the Bible, of the very first rainbow in the world.

It all happened a very long time ago. God was not at all pleased with the way many people were behaving. There was a great deal of wickedness in the world; lying and cheating, stealing and killing. God felt it was time that the people were taught a lesson. He decided to send a great flood that would cover the earth and the houses and even the mountains. God told Noah what he was going to do, because Noah was a good man and God didn't want to punish him.

Noah called his wife and his family to him. 'I have had a message from God', he said. 'We must build an ark out of wood, big enough and strong enough for us all to live in for as long as the great flood lasts. We must build it big enough to take animals, as well as ourselves. We must take two of every animal there is, so that when the flood is over, life can begin again.' Noah told his sons to get wood, and to begin making the ark. He told his wife to gather food for the family and for the animals; food to last a long time. He told his daughters to begin to collect together the animals; two of every known kind.

The work began as the weather worsened. Dark clouds began to gather and thunder rumbled in the distance. Noah knew that the rain and the flood would soon come. The family worked even harder so that everything would be ready when the storm broke. Noah went amongst the other villagers, telling them what was to happen, and asking them to give up their wicked lives, and to join him and his family in the safety of the ark. But no-one would listen to Noah. 'He's mad,' they said to each other, 'he's talking nonsense. There won't be a flood.'

Soon the wooden ark was finished. The family and food were safely inside. The animals were put into their special quarters on the ark. As the last animal went into its cage, the first drops of rain began to fall.

'It's Noah's flood', the people laughed, but a few days later they were laughing no longer. The rain beat down and made puddles, which made pools, which made lakes. The lakes joined together until no grass or ground was left uncovered. The people climbed to the roofs of their houses for safety, but soon the water was higher than the houses, and as high as the mountains. Only Noah and his family and the animals were safe inside the wooden, floating ark.

For forty days and forty nights the rain beat down, and then, quite suddenly, it stopped. Everything was quiet. Outside the ark there was not a sound to be heard. Noah opened a window and sent out a dove. It flew over the water, and came back with an olive leaf in its beak.

'There must be land nearby,' said Noah, 'land with earth and trees. Land for us to start our new life.'

Slowly, slowly, the flood water went down, and the ark came to rest on a mountain. Noah, his wife, their children, and all the animals climbed down from the ark to the earth. Noah knelt on the wet ground and looked up into the sky to say thank you to God for their safety. And there, high above them, was a beautiful, shimmering, sparkling rainbow; a message from God that he would always care for his people.

The story tells us that now, when we see a rainbow, it is a reminder from God of the flood, and a message to tell us he will always care.

Prayer

Thank you, God, for the beautiful colours around us.
Thank you for the colours of sunshine and the colours in showers.
Thank you for the beauty of a colourful, arching rainbow.
Make our eyes open to beauty around us in our world.

Amen

Hymn
'Sing a rainbow' **A**

The boy who cried wolf   *Week 8   Honesty*
adapted from Aesop

What would you say if I asked you what being honest means?

Yes, it means being honest with things: not stealing them. It means being honest with people when you're wrong: owning up if you have done something wrong, and saying you are sorry. It means being honest with words: telling the truth, not telling lies.

One of my favourite stories is about a boy who decided to tell a lie as a joke, but the joke didn't have a very happy ending.

Once upon a time there lived a boy, who had a job as a shepherd. Every day he had to take the village sheep along the lane, past the houses, up the hill, and into the green meadows high above where all the people lived. Sometimes the boy liked his job. He could lie on the grass in the sunshine, and daydream or sleep, as long as he kept a watchful eye on the sheep to make sure they were safe. But on other days, the boy would be bored. He had nothing to do, and no-one to talk to up there in the high pastures, and on those days, the time seemed endless until the evening when he could bring the sheep back down the hillside to the safety of the village for the night.

On one particular day, he was really fed-up. He felt lonely and bored.

'I wish I could think of something to liven things up a bit', he thought, as he lay on the grass staring down at the village.

'I know', he suddenly shouted as he jumped to his feet, 'I'll play a trick on them all. That'll be fun.'

The boy jumped onto a nearby rock, and shouted at the top of his voice, 'Help! Help! There's a wolf attacking the sheep. Help! Come quickly!'

The people in the houses below, heard the cry and rushed out of their houses and gardens. They grabbed sticks and farm tools on their way, and ran as fast as they could along the lane, up the hill and into the green meadows. They arrived, puffing and panting, ready to save the boy and the sheep from whatever wild animals were there.

Of course, when they arrived, there was no danger at all, and the boy was standing on his rock, laughing at them.

'That was a good trick', he spluttered. 'That made you all run, didn't it?'

The people didn't answer, but angrily turned on their heels and stamped back to their houses and gardens. They were not pleased to be made such fools of.

All was quiet for the next few days, and then, about a week later, the boy felt bored again. He remembered the trick he had played on the villagers, and remembered how they had all come running up the hill waving hoes and pitchforks and sticks. 'I'll do it again', chuckled the boy to himself. He jumped onto the rock again and began to shout as loudly as he could.

'Help! Come quickly! There's a fierce wolf attacking the sheep. Help me!'

Once again the people from the village rushed out of their houses, and ran along the lane, up the hill and into the green meadows to help the boy. Once again they found no wild animals and no danger: just the boy standing on the rock, laughing at them. Once again they crossly went back home.

Two days later, the boy was sitting propped against the rock, when he heard a sound – a dull, low growl, then a snarl. He felt the hair on the back of his neck prickle, and he suddenly felt very cold and very afraid. Slowly, he turned round, and looked straight into the angry, red eyes of a huge, grey wolf. The boy slowly crept backwards until the rock was between him and the wolf. Then he jumped up onto the rock and yelled at the top of his voice to the people in the village below. At the sound the wolf leapt amongst the sheep, killing them with his yellow fangs. The boy shouted and shouted until his throat hurt. He waved his arms and frantically begged for help.

The people in the village heard the boy.

'He needn't think he's going to trick us again', they said. 'He can shout until he loses his voice, but we're not going to be made fools of again', and they stayed in their homes and gardens.

One hour later, a very sorry-looking boy, with a tear-stained face, and torn clothes, covered in blood, trudged out of the green meadows down the hill, and along the lane, followed by a few sheep. The rest were lying dead in the green meadows.

'I'll never tell lies again', he said to the village people, 'I'm sorry.'

I think the boy kept his promise. He had learned that if you are always telling lies, people might not believe you when you tell the truth.

Prayer

Dear God, help us always to be honest in all things.
Help us to be truthful and not to tell lies.
Help us to help others to trust us.

Amen

Hymn
'When a knight won his spurs' **C&P**

Finders keepers   Week 8   Honesty

In our last assembly we said that there are lots of different ways of being honest: honest with things, honest with people, honest with words. We heard a story about a boy who told lies, and then realised how silly he had been to do that. Today's story is also about a boy. This time, a boy who found something one day.

The boy, and his mum and younger sister, had gone to the seaside for the day. They had set off quite early, and had caught the bus into town, where they had got on the coach which would take them to the sea.

Jasbinder had brought her bucket and spade and her favourite doll. Avtar hadn't brought anything except his pocket money, which was in his anorak pocket. All the way to the seaside, on the coach, Avtar had held the money with his hand in his pocket, and now the coins felt warm. He wished he had more spending money, he wanted to buy sweets and postcards, and he wanted to have turns on the amusement machines. He wondered if he would have enough, he knew his mum wouldn't give him any more, she was always saying she didn't have enough money.

When they arrived at the seaside town, everyone climbed down from the coach with their coats and bags, buckets and flasks, and set off walking towards the beach.

Avtar's mum saw a café. 'Come on,' she said, 'I'm thirsty, let's go and have a drink before we go on to the sands.' They trooped into the café, and Avtar was told to sit at a table and save three places, whilst Jasbinder and his mum went to buy tea and cokes. He slid along the red plastic bench, and then he saw it. It was pushed in the corner near the wall, a small brown purse, with a gold-coloured fastener. Avtar looked around, but no-one was watching; no-one looked as if they had lost a purse; no-one was taking any notice. He opened the purse and saw four pound coins, a five-pound note folded up, and some ten pence pieces. He looked around again, no-one was watching, so he quickly put the purse in his pocket and then put his arms on top of the table.

'No-one saw me,' he thought to himself, 'and anyway, no-one knows me here. I'll keep it.' But somehow, even with all that money in his pocket, he didn't feel happy. He knew it must belong to someone, and that they would be upset about losing it.

All day, while he was playing on the sand, paddling in the sea, having a picnic, and playing on the machines with his spending money, the thought of the purse in his pocket was niggling away in his mind. He knew it was wrong to keep it. He knew his mum would be cross if she knew it was in his pocket. The thought of the purse was spoiling his day a little, because the thought of it wouldn't go out of his head.

That night, in bed, Avtar took the purse out from under his pillow where he had hidden it when he got home. It looked at him, like a brown, round eye in his hand. 'Well, Finders Keepers', said Avtar to the purse. 'Whoever you belong to shouldn't have left you behind on the seat.' He tipped the money out onto the bedclothes. A small piece of card fell out together with the coins and the five-pound note. The card had a name and address on it in spidery writing. Avtar knew he should send the purse back to its owner, but he didn't want to. He gathered the money together, put it back in the purse and pushed the purse under his pillow again.

Avtar didn't sleep very well that night. The purse thoughts niggled away in his mind, just as they had during the day. In the morning he went into his mum's room early with the purse in his hand. 'Mum?' he said.

'I know', said his mum. 'I saw in the café, and I've been waiting to see what you would do. I'm glad you came to tell me.'

'Can we send it back?' asked Avtar, 'I know the address of the owner, it's inside.'

'I think that's a very good idea', answered his mum.

Avtar wrote a letter explaining that he'd found the purse in the café, then he and his mum posted the letter and purse, as a parcel.

Two weeks later a letter came in the post for Avtar. It had a five pound note in it as a reward for finding and returning the purse.

'I'm glad I didn't keep the purse, mum', said Avtar. 'I would have had more money If I'd kept it, but I wouldn't have felt as good about it.'

'I'm glad you were honest too', said his mum.

Avtar had a clear conscience because he knew he had been honest. I hope that if you find anything, you will try to find its owner. That is the honest thing to do.

Prayer

Dear God, help us to be honest with things we find.
Help us not to say 'finders keepers', but to try to find the owner,
so that we can return whatever was lost.

Amen

Hymn
'The journey of life' **C&P**

Jenny's nose
Week 8   Honesty

Once there was a little girl called Jenny, who was always telling lies. She could tell little lies, but often they were real 'whoppers'. Her mother, father, friends and teacher never knew whether to believe her or not. She was rather like the boy who cried wolf: she had told so many lies, that when she was telling the truth, people didn't believe her.

One day Jenny was in the kitchen drinking a glass of orange juice.

'Are you drinking something?' called her mum.

'No!' said Jenny. As she tipped up the glass to finish the drink, Jenny saw an eye looking at her from the thick glass base.

'It's time you were taught a lesson', said the eye. Jenny was so surprised to see the eye and to hear it speak, that she dropped the glass on to the floor, where it smashed to pieces, and she ran outside.

The next day Jenny's mum gave her some crisps to take to school. At playtime Jenny's friend asked if she would like to share her apple.

'Yes,' said Jenny, 'because my mum didn't give me anything to bring to school today!'

Suddenly, Jenny had the strangest feeling in her nose – a twitching, tickling, stretching feeling. Then she sneezed, coughed and hiccupped, and her nose grew about ten centimetres longer.

She tried very hard to take no notice of her new strange, longer nose; but it was difficult to ignore; she could see it with her own eyes.

At lunchtime it was Jenny's favourite pudding; chocolate sponge and mint custard. A teacher came along and asked Jenny if she had been given a second helping.

'No', said Jenny, even though she had eaten two second helpings. Suddenly, there was the strange feeling again; the twitching, tickling, stretching feeling. She sneezed, coughed and hiccupped, and her nose grew again. This time, Jenny covered it up with her hand.

During the afternoon, Jenny told lies to her teacher and her friends. She told a lie to her mum at hometime, and every time she said something untrue, her nose twitched, tickled and stretched, she sneezed, coughed and hiccupped, and her nose grew longer.

By tea-time, Jenny's nose was as long as a ruler, and she was miserable, sad, cross and unhappy. Her mum and dad took her to the doctor.

'Well, I've never seen anything like it', he said. 'Do you know why it's happening, Jenny?'

'No!' shouted Jenny, and her nose grew again.

She was sent to see a doctor at the hospital.

'No, I've never seen anything like it,' said the hospital doctor, 'do you know why, Jenny?'

'No!' shouted Jenny, and her nose grew again, there, right in front of their eyes.

'Ah!' whispered the doctor, 'I think I know why; something to do with telling lies.'

'I don't tell lies', said Jenny, and her nose grew again.

'There's nothing I can do to help', said the hospital doctor. 'Go home, and come back in a month.'

Jenny was taken home. It was awful. She couldn't eat or drink now. Her face ached. She couldn't go out to play or to school. She couldn't get through the door easily. Her nose was now as long as a metre stick.

That evening Jenny tried to have a drink of orange juice. She was by herself in the kitchen. As she looked into the bottom of the glass, there it was again, the eye, looking at her from the thick, heavy, glass base.

'Have you learned your lesson?' asked the eye.

Jenny started to cry. She cried and cried and tears dripped along the length of her nose, and fell off the end in a puddle.

'Yes', she said.

The strange feeling came again; her nose twitched and tickled and stretched, and then, slowly, slowly, bit by bit, it began to shrink. By breakfast time the next day, it was its normal size again.

Everytime that day, that Jenny spoke, she sneezed, coughed and hiccupped first. It was a reminder to tell the truth, and it worked. Jenny only told a few lies after that, and each time she did, she had the strangest feeling in her nose, and she knew she must tell the truth to make her nose shrink again.

I think Jenny was very unhappy when she was telling lies. People usually are when they know they are not telling the truth. Let's make sure we try to tell the truth. No-one here wants a nose that grows like Jenny's!

Prayer
> Help us, Lord, to be honest:
> Honest with words, help us to tell the truth,
> Honest when wrong, help us to own up bravely,
> Honest with things, help us not to take things which do not belong to us.
>
> *Amen*

Hymn
'Praise Him' **C&P**

The bees and the wasp   *Week 9   Actions speak louder than words*
adapted from Aesop

Some of you may know the name of this shape,* it has six sides; what is it? Yes, it's a hexagon. All shapes appear somewhere in nature, and this shape is made by bees. Bees build tiny hexagonal cells in their hives. The queen bee lays eggs into some of the cells, and those eggs hatch out into new bees. The worker bees make honey, and store it in more of the hexagonal cells. On the table this morning are some books about bees, and a tiny piece of honeycomb. If you look carefully, you will see the six-sided cells made out of bees wax, and you will see the golden liquid honey inside each cell.

In the bee hive, there are two kinds of bees; the worker bees and the drones. As you might guess, the worker bees are the ones that do all the work of the hive; keeping it clean, collecting pollen and nectar from the flowers, and making the honey for food. The drones have only one job to do; they fly with the queen bee on a sky-high flight, and then come back to the hive to do nothing.

The story this morning is about an argument that some worker bees had with the drones. The worker bees had been very busy making a particularly fine honeycomb. It was firm and fat, each tiny, beautifully made cell was full to the brim with sticky, sunshine honey. Some drones wandered past the honeycomb.

'That's a fine honeycomb we've made this morning', they said.

'It's a fine honeycomb, but you've not made it. We made it', answered the workers.

'Nonsense,' argued the drones, 'we made that honeycomb. We belong to this hive, and we made it.'

'That's not true and not fair', said the workers. 'We're the ones who work hard. We worked hard on that honeycomb and we made it, not you. You're too lazy to make a honeycomb at all, never mind one as fine as that.'

'We made it', insisted the drones.

'We need a judge to decide who is telling the truth', said one of the workers, and he went to ask a passing wasp.

'Please decide who is telling the truth', said the worker bee to the wasp. 'Please decide who it was who really made this honeycomb.'

The wasp looked at the honeycomb for a long time.

'Did you make it?' he said to the workers.

'Yes', said the worker bees.

'Did you make it?' the wasp asked the drones.

'Yes', answered the drones.

The wasp looked at the honeycomb again.

'You must each make another honeycomb', he said. 'Then I shall look at the new combs, one of them will be the same as this one, and we shall know who is telling the truth.'

'Good idea', said the workers, and straight away they scurried away to build a new honeycomb and fill it with honey.

'Oh, that's not fair', whined the drones, and they stood about in a group, grumbling and moaning.

Immediately, the wasp knew who had made the first honey comb. He knew, not by what the bees had said, but by their actions. The workers had been ready to build a new honeycomb because they knew they could. The drones were not prepared to build one, because they knew they couldn't, so they argued and made excuses instead.

'The workers own the honeycomb', said the wasp. 'The drones do not deserve honey', and he flew away home.

The workers, angry with the drones for lying about the building of the honeycomb, chased them out of the hive, and busily went back to their work.

Sometimes we can show by our actions what sort of people we are. When I was little, my mum used to say to me:

> 'There's a different way of doing things,
> A casual glance discloses:
> Some girls turn up their sleeves to work,
> And some turn up their noses!'

She meant that when we are asked to help, some of us get on well with the job, but others amongst us sometimes pull faces, and look as though we don't want to help!

Make sure your actions tell people what you really want them to know about you!

Prayer

> Dear God, please help us to work hard with our actions
> and not just with our voices.
>
> *Amen*

Hymn

'Who put the colours in the rainbow?' **C&P**

*I showed the children a large hexagonal template, but a cut-out paper shape or simply a drawing would do equally well. I gathered together a small collection of children's (and adult's) books on bees, for the small display, and added a pack of honeycomb – easily available from health food shops.

The witch and the dragon   *Week 9   Actions speak louder than words*

In our last assembly we heard that you can often show what sort of person you are, not by what you say but by what you do. If you watch other people, you can find out about them, by their actions, as well as by their words. Sometimes the actions and the words don't fit together, like in today's story. The actions say more than the words.

Once upon a time a witch and a dragon were next door neighbours in a wood. The witch lived in a gingerbread house and the dragon lived in a cave cut out of a rock. Every day, people from the village walked past the witch's house and the dragon's house, on their way to and from the town.

When people passed the witch's house, they always stopped to say hello, and she would smile at them and say in a sweet voice, 'Hello, how nice to see you today.' But when people passed the dragon's house, they would hurry by because he looked so fierce and growled when anyone came near.

One summer, two new children called Mark and Emma came to live in the village and they had to walk past the two houses every day on their way to school. They watched the other children talking to the witch at her door and hurrying past the dragon at his. And one day they watched something else as well.

Mark and Emma watched the witch as she spoke and they saw a glint and a gleam in her beady black eyes. They saw her take a strange wizened apple out of her apron pocket, and offer it to one of the children. They saw her smile a crooked, wicked smile as the child took the fruit.

'Did you see that?' said Mark. 'She sounds all nice and friendly, but she doesn't *look* very friendly does she?'

Just then the witch stretched out thin and bony fingers and grasped a handful of Emma's long hair.

'What a pretty child and what pretty hair', simpered the witch in a soft voice, but all the time she was speaking she was twisting and pulling the hair.

'Ow, she's not behaving in a very friendly way either', said Emma, and she squirmed out of the way as the witch let go.

Mark pulled Emma away from the witch's door and stood with her near the dragon's door.

'Come on,' said Emma, 'come away. I'm scared. He's fierce and growly. He's even worse than that horrid witch.'

'Just a minute,' said Mark, 'look.'

They both looked in through the dragon's open door, and then looked at each other in astonishment. The dragon was sitting in a chair inside his house, and on his knee was a tiny kitten. The dragon was growling softly, but the noise was almost like a purr. The dragon was very gently stroking the kitten and tickling it under its chin. The kitten stretched and yawned and rolled over onto its back. It wasn't at all afraid of the huge dragon.

'He's not fierce at all', said Mark. 'Look how gentle he is with the kitten. Let's say hello to him.' The two children called to the dragon and he came to the doorway, still carefully cradling the kitten.

'Why don't you talk to people when they walk past your house?' asked Emma.

'They don't seem to want to talk to me,' growled the dragon in a gruff voice. 'I think it's because I growl a lot.'

'We'll talk to you every day if you want us to', said Mark.

The dragon looked at Mark and Emma, and then he smiled a long, slow, wide smile.

'I'd like that', he said.

Soon all the people from the village began to talk to the dragon, and they all realised that behind his growling voice, was a kind, gentle, thoughtful creature. They also realised that the witch, behind her nice words, was quite spiteful and mean, so they stopped talking to her on their way through the wood and soon she packed her belongings on her broomstick and flew away to find a new house. The dragon lost his next door neighbour, but he had found lots of new friends, and was happy for the first time in his life.

Emma and Mark found out that people show what they are really like by their behaviour, not just by their words. Sometimes people's behaviour tells more about them than any amount of words.

Prayer

Dear God, help us to know that actions speak louder than words.
Help us not to be fooled by nice words, if those nice words are not true.

Amen

Hymn

'Think think on these things' **SSL**

Passing the parcel

Week 9   Actions speak louder than words

I can look at you now, and I can tell a great deal about you, just by watching your actions. I can tell, just by looking, whether you are quiet and well-behaved, or whether you are a chattery person, who shuffles a lot!

During the last few weeks, you have all been out on school visits, and you know that people have been able to tell what our school is like, just by watching you, because actions can say a lot about you.

On Saturday, I went to a party, and I discovered that people's actions were very important there. The party was at my neighbour's house and I went along and knocked at the door at the time I had been asked to go. Mary, my neighbour, asked me in, and there were already lots of people there, all talking and laughing. There were children playing a game, and grown-ups talking about gardening and TV programmes and children's schools: all those things which grown-ups usually talk about when they get together. But the strangest thing was, there wasn't a sound. Even though lots of people were all talking at the same time, there wasn't a sound to be heard.

A little later on, everyone got ready to play 'pass the parcel'. Now, you all know how to play 'pass the parcel' and I thought I knew how to play it. I sat in the circle and I waited for the music to begin. But, quite suddenly, the parcel started going round, everyone passing it on to the next person, without any music at all. Suddenly, the lights went on, the parcel stopped, and the little girl who had it at that moment, began tearing off a layer of paper. Someone turned the lights off again and the parcel went on its journey. Still there was no music.

'It's a funny sort of pass the parcel', I thought to myself. 'How do people know when to take off a wrapping if there is no music to tell them.' Suddenly the lights went on again at exactly the same moment that the parcel was pushed into my hands. Almost without thinking, I began to take off a layer of paper as quickly as I could. I had just pulled off one sheet of paper, when the lights went off and I passed the parcel on to the person next to me. I understood what was happening. We were not playing pass the parcel to music, we were playing it to the lights. Someone was turning the light switch off and on, and that was telling people when it was their turn to take off a layer of wrapping paper. I had never played pass the parcel like that before. Soon the game was finished, and a small boy won the box of sweets in the middle of the parcel.

Next it was time for tea, a lovely tea with sausage rolls, sandwiches, crisps, cakes, jellies and ice-cream. Everyone began to talk to each other again as they ate their tea. But, once again, although everyone was talking, there wasn't a sound to be heard.

Can you guess why there was no noise when people talked, and why we played pass the parcel in that unusual way?

Yes, it was because nearly all the people at the party were deaf. They couldn't hear, and so they used sign language to speak to each other. They couldn't hear music for pass the parcel, and so they used the lights as a signal instead.

I don't know how to speak using sign language, but I tried to learn a few signs so that I could at least say something to the people who were deaf.

Even though those people at the party were deaf, they could still talk to each other, and have fun, just like you do when you go to a party.

If you think about it, I think you will find that even though we can hear, we quite often use actions to make ourselves understood. In school the teachers sometimes use actions instead of words to ask you to do something. They might ask you to sit down, or wait, or be quiet, just by doing an action. You can probably tell what your teacher or mum is thinking, just by watching the expression on their face. They might be saying 'well done', or 'I'm cross', or 'I don't understand'; but they might say it without actually speaking the words.

Actions are important. They can say so much about you. Good and bad behaviour, kindness and unkindness, happiness and anger, can all be shown by your actions.

We must make sure that our actions say the right thing about us.

Prayer

Dear God, thank you for our bodies and our hands,
which make actions.
Thank you for our faces, which show our expressions.
Thank you for our brains, which tell our bodies
to make the actions we want.
Help us to make sure that our actions tell people
what we want them to know about us.

Amen

Hymn
'If you're happy and you know it' **A**

The lapwing field   *Week 10   Being observant*

What does being observant mean? Yes, it means keeping our eyes open, and looking carefully, and noticing things. Sometimes we only see what we expect to see; we don't notice unusual or different things, but if we keep our eyes open, we might be surprised at what we see, as today's story shows. This is a true story; it happened to me.

At the bottom of my garden is a huge field and this year there are lapwings in the field.* One day, not very long ago, I was standing at the fence at the bottom of the garden, watching the lapwings. Two of them were spending a lot of time flying together, and one of them was showing off doing a twisting, tumbling flight and making a lot of noise. I looked at them through the binoculars and realised they were a pair of lapwings, who were probably going to build a nest in the field, lay eggs and raise a clutch of baby lapwings. I felt very excited, because although I'd seen lots of adult lapwings, I had never seen a nest, or any baby lapwings before.

Every day I went to the fence and looked through the binoculars, but I couldn't see the nest. One day I climbed over the fence to take a closer look in the field, but the birds flew off. I didn't find a nest, and I didn't want to frighten the birds away completely, so I came out of the field. I decided that I wouldn't be able to see the nest, or the eggs, or the baby birds, so I would just have to be content with knowing they were there, even though I couldn't see them. And that was that, I thought.

A few days later, having almost forgotten about the lapwings, I went for a day out to Knowsley Safari Park. I was looking forward to seeing the lions and tigers, the elephants and camels, the bison and kangaroos and deer. Those were the creatures I expected to see.

I drove in through the huge gates of the Safari Park. Ahead of me was the road leading through a large field, and in the distance were the first Safari Park animals: massive bison with long shaggy coats. The other cars behind me hurried past on their way to the animals, but I was going slowly because I had seen something else. As well as the bison, this field, like my field at home, had lapwings in it. I stopped the car at the edge of the road for a few minutes to watch the birds. The other cars carried on driving past, but I wasn't in a hurry.

I looked out across the field and watched the lapwings flying and landing. And then I looked down at the grassy edge of the road just next to where

I was sitting. A female lapwing was standing there making a very loud noise at my car. When she saw that neither my car, nor I was going to hurt her, she stopped squawking and turned to go to a small heap of stones. But they weren't stones. They were eggs. There, right in front of my eyes was a lapwing's nest. I sat perfectly still and looked and looked. I saw a tiny lapwing chick, just newly hatched, and all wet and bedraggled: its egg shell was still in the nest. The mother lapwing picked up the pieces of shell one by one, carried them out of the nest and threw them down a little way away: she was cleaning the nest. I saw two other lapwing chicks just outside the nest. They were about two days old and round, soft, grey and fluffy. They walked on wobbly legs. I saw one lapwing egg, just waiting to hatch.

I spent a long time just watching the lapwings and the nest, and I thought how I'd nearly missed seeing it. If I hadn't stopped to watch the birds I wouldn't have looked down at the road edge, and I wouldn't have seen the nest.

All the time I'd been watching the nest, the other drivers had hurried past, and they had all missed that little bit of new life in the Safari Park. I followed the Safari road, and enjoyed seeing all the animals, but for me, the best part was seeing the lapwing's nest; the part I hadn't expected to see, and the part I only noticed by being observant.

Every day, all through our lives, there are exciting new things to see. We need to keep our eyes open, to look around us, to be observant, so that we don't miss seeing those things.

Prayer

Thank you, God, for our eyes.
Help us to use our eyes carefully so that we see things
    that are not easily seen at first.

Amen

Hymn
'I have seen the golden sunshine' **SSL**

*I showed the children an illustration of a lapwing. I used the full page illustration in 'Birds of Town and Village' (Country Life Books ISBN 0 600 430219) because of its clarity, size and the inclusion of nest and eggs; but any other illustration would suffice, and could be left out for closer inspection by the children after the assembly.

Mrs O'Reilly

Being observant means watching and looking and noticing. If we're observant we see things that other people might miss; we learn things; we become better at reading and writing and painting because looking at things carefully gives us inspiration; gives us ideas. It's usually the children who look at things and notice things who do best in their work at school. Being observant even made the person in today's story quite famous.

Mrs O'Reilly was quite an ordinary mum, except that she had a bigger-than-usual family. She had Mr O'Reilly, ten children, two dogs, three cats, a hamster, a canary in a cage, and four fish in a gold fish bowl; so you can imagine, she was a very busy person.

Mrs O'Reilly was up every morning early, to begin her day's work; and work she did. She cooked and cleaned, washed and ironed, polished and mended for all the people in her family. Now Mrs O'Reilly was a very organised person; she had to be with such a large family to care for, and she always did her jobs at certain times of the day and on certain days of the week. For instance, if you went to her house at half-past-ten on a Monday morning, you would find her in the middle of a huge pile of washing. The baby and smallest children would be playing on the floor, and she would be up to her elbows in soapy, sudsy water. If you went to her house at two o'clock on a Wednesday afternoon, you would find her in the middle of a huge batch of baking. The baby and the smallest children would be 'helping' her by tasting, and she would be up to her elbows in floury pastry and crunchy biscuit mix.

Nothing ever changed in Mrs O'Reilly's life, everything stayed the same, until one day her youngest child started school. 'I don't know what I'm going to do now,' she said to the headteacher on that day, 'my house won't be the same without children in it all day. There'll just be me at home now, everyone else is away in the day.'

'You'll find something to do,' said the headteacher, 'something will turn up.'

Mrs O'Reilly went home to her spick and span and empty house, even the cats and dogs were out playing in the garden; she was all alone. She looked out of the window, thinking she'd have a cup of coffee then start her ironing. She noticed the postman go to the house opposite.

'He's early today', she thought.

Mrs O'Reilly knew at exactly what time everyone in the street came and went. She knew who went out to work and who didn't. She knew at what time people came and went, because she was observant. She noticed these things.

Mrs O'Reilly looked across at the opposite house again. The postman was nowhere to be seen, but the front door was open a little.

'That's funny', she thought. 'They all go out to work at eight o'clock, and I know they've gone today because I saw them setting off.' She looked carefully at the front of the house. She saw a tiny twitch of a curtain, a dim shadow of a movement and then stillness. The hair on the back of her neck prickled as she thought 'Burglars!' Not taking her eyes off the front of the house, she moved to her hallway and reached for the 'phone. She could see the house now through her own front door. She rang the house's number.

She could hear the 'phone ringing in the house opposite, then a crash as though the noise had suddenly startled someone and made them drop something. She put her 'phone down. Silence. She picked it up again and rang the police. In no time they were there, pulling up outside the house in a police car. Two men rushed out of the front door, jamming each other in the doorway in their haste to escape. The police grabbed them and took them away in the car. The postman was found, tied up in a heap on the hall floor.

'Well done Mrs O'Reilly', said the police later. 'If it hadn't been for you being observant, these burglars would have got away with half the house, and the poor postman might have been tied up there all day. He called too early and caught them at it, so they dragged him inside and tied him up.'

Mrs O'Reilly smiled. Her dull day had turned out to be quite exciting, and although she didn't know it yet, it was going to be the start of something even more exciting.

'It was as good as a story', she told her family at teatime later that day. And that gave her an idea. The next day she got out a pencil and some paper and started to write the first Burglar Ben story. Soon both the stories and Mrs O'Reilly were famous: and all because Mrs O'Reilly had used her eyes and been observant.

If you keep your eyes open, and are observant, you will see something that will give you a good idea for a painting or a model or a story. Keep looking!

Prayer
Thank you, God, for our eyes and brains.
Help us to be observant and not to go about with our eyes closed
to exciting things which happen around us.

Amen

Hymn
'He made me' **C&P**

The fox and the goat
adapted from Aesop

Week 10   Being observant

Being observant and looking carefully is very good, but it's even better if you use your brain and think as well. It's no good just seeing something if you don't think about what you've seen. Today's story is about two animals. They could both see, but one of them did a bit more thinking than the other one. The one who wasn't very observant, and who didn't think either, didn't have a very happy time.

Once upon a time a fox found a well. It was quite a deep well but it had clear water in the bottom and the fox was thirsty. He leaned as far as he could over the low wall around the well, and the next thing he knew he had fallen in with an almighty splash. Luckily the water wasn't very deep, so the fox didn't drown. He stood there up to his ears in water wondering what to do next.

'Well! I'll have a drink now I'm here, then I'll climb out', he decided. But he soon discovered that was easier said than done. The sides of the well were steep and slippery with slime. Each time he tried to climb out he slid down again into the water. He tried to jump, but the water weighed him down and he couldn't spring high enough.

'I'll just have to stay down here until someone comes along to help me out', he said to the echoey walls of the well.

After a little while, a goat came wandering by, looked into the well, and said, 'What are you doing down there?'

The fox looked at the goat and thought, 'She's not very observant: she's not noticed how slippery and slimy the walls are, she doesn't realise I'm stuck down here and I can't get out; I can play a trick on her.'

'I'm having a drink', he shouted up at the goat. 'This is the best water for miles around. It's deliciously cool and clear. Why don't you join me down here, I'll share it with you.'

'How very kind', answered the silly goat, and without bothering to look or think, she jumped into the well. She had a long drink and then looked around to see how to get out.

'How do we do it?' she asked.

'Easy', said the fox. 'You stand on your back legs and stretch up the wall as far as you can with your front legs. I climb on your back, stand on your shoulders, and then I will just about be able to reach the ground to climb out. Er, then I'll pull you out.'

'How very kind', said the silly goat again, but she didn't notice the mischievous glint in the fox's beady eye. She didn't think to wonder what she would do if the fox didn't help her. She simply did as the fox had suggested. She stood up on her hind legs and stretched her front legs as far up the slippery walls as she could reach.

The fox climbed onto her back, stood on her shoulders, gripped the edge of the well with his paws and hoisted himself out. Then he ran away across the field as fast as his legs would carry him, shouting, 'Next time, be a bit more observant. Look before you leap, you silly goat.'

The poor goat was left standing there in the water at the bottom of the well for the rest of the day. Luckily for her, just before dark, a man came by and pulled her out.

I think the goat learned her lesson. I hope she did. I hope no-one in our school would be silly enough to jump into something without looking and thinking very carefully first.

Prayer
> Dear God, help us please to be observant,
> and to look before we leap.
> Help us to think of the consequences of what we do.
>
> *Amen*

Hymn
'Hands to work and feet to run' **C&S**

Sports' day
Week 11   Summer days

This week we will be having our Sports' days at school. Sports' days are times for fun, enjoyment and excitement, days when we hope everyone will have a good time and join in. I think that's the best thing about Sports' days – everyone taking part and joining in – it's much more important than actually winning races, although winning can be fun as well.

Sometimes when people take part in a race they just keep their eyes on the winning post and concentrate on getting there first. That's all right as long as they don't completely forget about everybody else. I know a story about someone who ran a race, and *did* forget about everyone else.

Once upon a time a group of messengers in Caesar's empire were quarrelling about which of them was the fastest runner. In those days in ancient Rome important messages were sent by men and boys either on horseback or by foot. The messages that were sent to people within the city were always sent by runners, and there was great competition amongst them as to who was the fastest. They knew that the speediest runner would be Caesar's favourite, and would be rewarded well.

'There is only one way to settle this,' said one of the runners, 'we will have a race.' The arrangements were made and at dawn the next morning eight runners and a huge crowd gathered at the arena for the race. Each one of the eight runners was anxious to win. Each one knew how important it was to be Caesar's favourite and fastest messenger. Each one was determined to reach the winning post first.

They lined up at the start of the track. The starter lifted his arm high in the air, the runners gripped their toes to the ground; ready; off. They surged forward all together, legs pounding the earth. Brutus glanced to left and right, Julius and Claudius were overtaking him, yet he was determined he was going to win. Brutus pushed his elbows out and nudged Julius out of the way. Julius looked startled for a moment, but in that moment Brutus ran ahead. Just Claudius to deal with now; the others were behind. Brutus put every bit of energy he had into reaching Claudius. He drew level with him and kicked out with his foot. Claudius rolled over on the ground with a groan. The winning post was now just a few strides away, but Julius was catching up with Brutus. Again Brutus pushed out his elbows and caught Julius in his chest, making him stumble and almost fall. Brutus didn't care, he was there, he was first past the winning post. He was the fastest.

Brutus smiled triumphantly at the crowd and waited for the shouts and cheers and applause, but it didn't come. Just a few half-hearted claps from Brutus' own friends were to be heard. The shouts and cheers came for the next runners past the winning post, the runners who had not cheated, but who had done their best and run well. The crowd felt sorry for Julius and Claudius who had had their chances in the race spoiled by a cheat. The crowd felt angry with Brutus.

Suddenly Brutus was ashamed. He had no joy in winning the race because he knew he had not won fairly. He wished he could be one of the losers: they knew they had done their best and the crowd was clapping them for trying. Brutus knew he would never cheat again in any race. Quietly he went away and spent many days on his own.

Brutus learned the hard way, that it's not just winning that matters. The important part of any race is how you run it. If you have taken part and done your best you are one of the winners, and you can be proud of yourself.

Prayer

Dear God, life is like a race in which we all take part.

Help us to take our part and do our best in all the races of our lives.

Amen

Hymn

'One more step' **C&P**

The holiday   *Week 11   Summer days*

One of the best things about summer time is holidays. Lots of people like to go somewhere different from where they live for one or two weeks, for a change. Living somewhere different is always fun. I think lots of you will perhaps have had a holiday in a caravan or tent, a boat, or hotel or a cottage. Some of you will have stayed in a house or flat in another city or even another country. You don't have to go away of course to have a holiday. Sometimes we have holidays at home; the days are different from ordinary days because we don't go to school or work, we can do other things instead.

People haven't always had holidays. A hundred years ago, ordinary people worked all the time and didn't have days off to go on holiday. Even very rich people didn't have holidays as we do today. The person in today's story took his family on the first holiday of their lives.

Prince Radleigh was a somewhat selfish boy. He was the son of the King and Queen of Beldumpia and was quite used to having his own way. Unfortunately his mother and father usually gave him absolutely everything he asked for, and everyone knows that the happiest children are not those who always get what they want.

Beldumpia was a small kingdom in the middle of a group of mountains, and although Prince Radleigh had visited everywhere in Beldumpia itself, he had never been to any other kingdom.

One day, some travellers came through Beldumpia on their way from one kingdom to another, and they called at the palace to deliver a message from the neighbouring king.

Prince Radleigh met them in the courtyard.

'Where have you come from?' he asked.

'We've come from the seaside', they said.

'The seaside,' said the Prince, 'I've never heard of that kingdom. Where is it?'

The travellers laughed, 'It isn't a kingdom, it's anywhere next to the sea.'

'What is the sea?' asked the Prince.

The travellers looked at one another in amazement. 'Do you not know what the sea is?' they said.

When they realised that the Prince had never seen the sea and didn't even know what it was, they told him all about it.

'I want to go and visit the sea', said Prince Radleigh. 'I want to go and live near it for one week, and then come home again.'

Well of course, because the prince wanted it, it had to be done. The King and Queen had to make all sorts of arrangements. The prince wanted all the servants, all the palace furniture, all his friends, his toys, his animals, everything he usually had around him to go to the seaside as well. A whole army of removal trucks had to be brought in to carry everything the prince would need for his one week visit to the seaside.

On his first morning by the sea, the prince wanted to go on the beach. He could see people digging and making sand pies and he wanted to do that as well. Of course, because the prince wanted it, it had to be done: but the prince didn't want to go on the beach on his own. Oh no! He wanted everyone to go with him; all the servants, all his friends, his toys, his animals, his parents, everyone.

At last everyone was settled on the beach, and the prince changed his mind. He wanted to go in the sea, but he didn't want to go on his own. Oh no! He wanted everyone to go with him; all the servants, all his friends, his toys, his animals, his parents, everyone. And of course, because the prince wanted it, it had to be done.

No sooner had the prince got into the sea, than he wanted to come out. Then he wanted to ride on the donkeys, visit the zoo, go on a boat, sit in the park, feed all the ducks, and then he wanted to go back on the beach. Each time he wanted to do something he wanted everyone else to do it too, and of course because he wanted it, it had to be done.

By the end of the week at the seaside Prince Radleigh had had a wonderful time, but everyone else was exhausted. 'Never-ever-ever-again', they all said when they got back to Beldumpia. 'Never-ever-again.'

I wonder if Prince Radleigh was taken on holiday again. I don't think he deserved to go again, do you?

When we go on holiday, we need to remember that the holiday belongs to other people in our family, as well as ourselves. We must try not to be selfish.

Prayer

Thank you, God, for holidays.
Whether we have holidays at home or holidays away,
help us to help everyone we are with to have a happy time.

Amen

Hymn
'Sing for joy' **SFJ**

Holiday house at Silverdale   *Week 11   Summer days*

Summer days means trips and visits and picnics, hopefully in warm sunny weather. Everyone usually feels good if they've had a day out in the fresh air and sunshine at the seaside or in the country. People who live in big cities and towns especially like to go on summer visits. Today I have a true story about some children who lived in a big city nearly a hundred years ago. They weren't able to go on trips or picnics because they were too poor.

Leeds, nearly a hundred years ago, was a smoky city full of factories and rows of tiny brick houses all touching each other back-to-back. There were some big houses with gardens on the edge of the city of course, but they were for the richer people. The poor people lived in the middle of the city where the factories and mills were. Whole families lived in houses that had only one or two rooms. They didn't have proper bathrooms or inside toilets. They had to share a water pump with a lot of other families, and carry water back into their houses. They had to share a toilet with other families. The children, even those as young as some of you, had to go out to work in the factories or mills or big houses.

One day some ladies were talking to a group of children from the poorest homes. The children looked dirty and tired, pale and ill.

'You need to get out into the fresh air and the sunshine', said one of the ladies.

The children stared at her. They hardly knew what fresh air was; they spent their lives breathing dusty factory air, and even when they were outside, the air was full of smoke and soot. They hardly ever saw any sunshine. Their houses and streets were dark, gloomy places.

'You should go and have a holiday at the seaside or in the countryside', said another lady.

The children stared at her as well. Not one of them had ever been to the seaside or to the country. They couldn't go. Their mothers and fathers were too poor to take them. Some of the mothers didn't have enough money for bread, never mind holidays. Some of the fathers were ill or out of work and had no money at all.

The ladies realised that holidays for these children were impossible. After all, Leeds was 60 miles from the sea; it was a long, long way. Then one of them said, 'If we raised some money and bought a house by the sea, we could take these children on holiday. We could take lots of poor children to the seaside. We could take different children every week, and fill the house with children for the whole of the summer.'

'Do you really think we could do that?' asked another lady.

'We could try', the first one said.

And try they did. They told all their friends of their plan. They raised money for the holiday plan and asked their friends to raise money too. They asked the rich people in Leeds to give money towards the children's holidays. Then they went to the seaside to look for a house to use as the holiday home. They searched, but couldn't find a suitable house. Then they found a piece of land at Silverdale, in beautiful countryside looking over the sea at Morecambe. It was just right – countryside and seaside all rolled into one.

'We'll buy it', said the ladies, 'then we'll build a house.' Not only did they build a house, but a swimming pool, a sports' hall and playing fields as well. Soon everything was ready. A warden and a matron were moved into the house to look after the children. The first ones arrived for their first-ever holiday. They came in their poor, dirty, city clothes, carrying their few possessions in paper bags. At first they were shy and a little homesick, but by the end of the week they were happy, healthy, sunburned children who had made lots of new friends and had a wonderful time. All through that first summer they came, needy children of Leeds coming for a free holiday at Silverdale.

The holiday plan had worked.

Today that same holiday plan is still working, but it isn't just for poor children. Any children in Leeds who *need* a holiday can have a chance of spending two weeks at the seaside; and the people of Leeds, just like the ladies at the beginning of the story, help to raise money to pay for the holiday house at Silverdale.

Prayer

Thank you, God, for the seaside and the countryside.
Thank you for holidays, visits and picnics.
Thank you for happy summer days.

Amen

Hymn
'Join with us' **C&P**

Just one step   *Week 12   Taking steps*

If I want to walk from here where I am standing, to the wall, I have to start by taking a step. If I wanted to walk from here to the playground, I would have to start by taking a step; and if I wanted to walk from here, all round the world and back, I would have to start by taking one step.

All journeys, whether they are long or short, all start with a single step.

Once upon a time there was a man who was very ill in hospital. The man had something wrong with his leg, and the doctors were unable to make it better. They had to operate on him and amputate his leg. If they hadn't done that, the man would have died.

After the operation, the man was in a great deal of pain, and everyone said he would never be able to walk again. When he felt better, he would have to sit in a wheelchair all the time.

'I will walk again', said the man. 'I will have an artificial leg and I will walk again.' His friends looked at him with sad faces. 'He won't,' they said, 'he won't.'

The man spent the next few months working very hard at his exercises. Each day he grew a little stronger, and when he was fitted with his artificial leg he began to learn to walk again, just a few steps at a time. It was very difficult.

When his friends saw him walking a little they said, 'It's very good, but of course he'll never be able to walk far. He'll only be able to walk around the house', and they looked at him once more with sad faces.

'One day I will walk the length of England,' said the man, 'just you wait and see.'

His friends didn't believe him; after all, it's a long way from the north of England to the south.

The man kept on working hard at walking. Each day he became more determined to fulfil his dream of walking the length of England.

At last he decided he was strong enough to try. He knew the journey would be difficult and that it would take him many weeks. He knew he might not succeed, but he was going to try.

The journey began with just one step, then another and another and another. The man walked for a whole day and slept that night at a friend's house. The next day he set out again. By now people had heard about his walk and they wanted to help. They offered him places to sleep each night. They sponsored him on the walk and he decided the money should be given to the hospitals to help other disabled people. Each day he found new friends, and each day took him a little further on his journey.

When he had been walking for ten days, he had an accident and fell. An ambulance came and took him to the nearest hospital.

'Well, that's the end of that,' said his friends, 'he'll stop walking now.'

'I shall not stop until I have walked across England', answered the man. After two days in hospital he set off again. Twenty days later he collapsed in the road and had to have doctors to help him up.

'Surely he'll give up now', said his friends; but of course the man didn't give up. He walked on again after a few days in hospital.

He walked steadily and slowly, step by step, day after day, and he made it. He walked all the way from the north of England to the sea in the south. He walked onto the sand and dipped his foot in the water.

'I did it,' he said to his friends, 'I told you I would and I did.'

'We don't know how', said his friends.

'Every journey, no matter how long or short, starts with just one step', said the man. 'I took my first step and simply carried on and did my best.'

The man succeeded because he set off and did his best. When you step out of your old class at the end of this week, please do your best, whether you are taking a small step into a new class at our school, or a big step into a new school. Do your best at every step.

Prayer

Soon we will be taking the next step in our school lives.
Help us, Lord, to step out bravely and to do our best.

Amen

Hymn
'The journey of life' **C&P**

Moonstep

Week 12   Taking steps

In our last assembly we heard about a man who started a journey with just one step. I know another story about a man who took just one step, but this was one of the most important and famous steps ever taken. It was so famous it was on television , and I can remember staying up one whole night to watch it as it happened. It was on July 21st 1969.

The story really started several years earlier when a group of men started a special training course in America. It was rather like a special kind of school, but instead of learning how to read and write, these men were learning how to be astronauts. They knew that if they worked hard and did their best they might be chosen for a very special project. They were not sure exactly what the project was going to be, but they knew it was important and that it had never been done before.

The men had to follow a very difficult training programme. They exercised to become really fit and strong; they learned how to work all the complicated controls on a space module; they were taught how to walk and move about in huge heavy spacesuits; they practised being weightless in special machines. That was one of the hardest things to become used to. The men's bodies became very light as gravity was taken away in the weightless compartment. Instead of standing on the floor or sitting in a chair, the men found themselves floating about. Everything else, cups, plates, food, even water, floated about as well. It was very strange. The men had to learn to eat special pre-packed food and to drink special liquid food and water out of tubes.

At last the long training programme was over and the men were ready to travel into space. They knew that only four of them would be chosen. The others would be reserves and would perhaps have a chance to go on the next expedition to space. They waited to hear who was going and where in space they were travelling to.

'This is a very special project', said the organiser. 'You are not just going into space, you are going to be the first men ever to go to the moon. You will land on the moon and be the first human beings to walk on it.' Then he told the men which of them had been chosen. They were delighted, the mission was even more exciting than they had dreamed. Just think – to be the first people to set foot on the moon.

At last the day of the rocket launch arrived. Huge crowds gathered to watch and the whole launch was televised. 10, 9, 8, 7, 6, 5, 4, 3, 2, 1, 0, lift off. The rocket slowly forced its way off the launching pad. The gantry fell away in a cloud of dust and gas. The rocket gathered speed with a tremendous burst of energy and thrust its way into the clear sky.

'We have lift off plus sixty', said a voice, and the rocket was already disappearing into the distance of space.

It took some time for the rocket to travel to the moon and boost itself into the moon's orbit. Once in orbit the astronauts prepared to launch the lunar module from the mother ship. It was successful and the module dropped quietly onto the surface of the moon. Its wide feet sank into moondust, the astronauts had arrived.

Slowly the lunar module door opened and a step ladder poked its way to the ground. Neil Armstrong, the first astronaut, climbed in his spacesuit onto the first step. Down he climbed, step by step, until he was just one step away from the moon's surface. No-one had ever set foot here before, his step was to be the first step ever made by man, on the moon. He stretched out his foot and placed it firmly on the moon.

'That's one small step for a man, one giant leap for mankind', he said.

Soon the astronauts were running and jumping, hopping and bouncing, near to the lunar module. They collected samples of rock and stones, and went for a ride in their moon buggy. Then, sadly, it was time to leave and begin the journey back to the mother ship, still in orbit above them, and then home.

A few days later, the astronauts safely arrived back on earth. The project was a huge success.

Those important words spoken by Neil Armstrong have become some of the most famous words ever spoken. The words were very true: the step was a small one for a man to take, but taking the first step on the moon was very important for mankind.

Prayer
> Dear God, thank you for brave people, like Neil Armstrong,
> who take important steps for mankind.
> Soon we will be taking steps into new classes and new schools.
> Help us to take those steps bravely.
> *Amen*

Hymn
'Tomorrow' **SFJ**

One more step

Week 12   Taking steps

Prior to the assembly, using the school log book and diary, I chose something of note that had happened in each month since September. These observations I wrote on pieces of card, the reverse of which carried the name of the month in letters large enough to be visible to all the children. Our school observations included starting new classes, team events, social events, Christmas activities, arrival of new staff, weather conditions, open days, visits, etc. A child read out the observations for each month at the point marked with an asterisk below.

In the very first assembly of this school year, we had some children doing a jigsaw. Today's assembly reminds me of a jigsaw, because today we are fitting in the last piece of our school year. We can look back now on one whole year; it had all fitted into place, and today is the last little bit of the year to be fitted in, like the last piece of a jigsaw.

If you have a very good memory, you will remember that we looked at the school log book at the beginning of the year. We saw all the empty pages that were waiting to be filled with this school year's happenings. Let's look back and see what we have done during this year.*

Our school year has been rather like a journey. In September we took our first step. We didn't know exactly what would happen at each step on our journey, but every day we took another step into our school year. Today our year is ended and we are ready to take more steps into the future.

We hope the children who are leaving our school today will step out bravely and be happy in their new schools.

We hope the teachers who are leaving today have enjoyed travelling this part of their journey with us, and will be happy in the future.

We hope everyone will have a safe and happy holiday.

I am looking forward to the holiday, but I am looking forward to seeing our school family again in September, and starting a new year's journey.

Prayer

Thank you, God, for fun and friends, and fellowship.
Thank you for a happy year at school.
Thank you for the friends we have made, the things we have learned,
and the things we have done.
Help us all to have a safe and happy holiday,
and help us to step out bravely and do our best in the next school year.

Amen

Hymn
'One more step' **C&P**

Alphabetical index of stories

Theme index – other than main themes listed in contents.